.RED ACROSS THE SEA

Published By

SONS OF NORWAY

1455 West Lake Street

Minneapolis, Minnesota

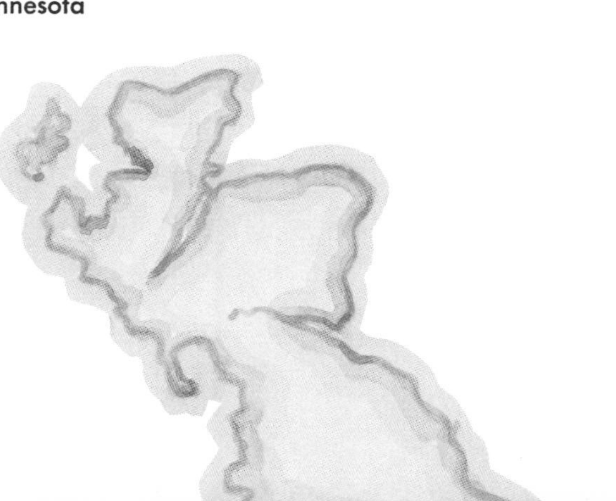

SONS OF NORWAY

SONG BOOK

A collection of Norway's most popular Folk Songs, Patriotic Songs and Ballads. Arranged for ensemble singing as well as solo voice and piano.

NORWEGIAN AND ENGLISH TEXTS.

Price $3.95

PREFACE

The international fraternal benefit society, Sons of Norway, published a song book with Norwegian lyrics in 1926, entitled "SØNNER AF NORGE SANGBOG," which was compiled by Carsten Woll, and which contained some 150 songs, including some of the more popular American songs. This song book was published at that time because it had been difficult to obtain a collection of Norwegian songs with music that was suitable for community singing. In 1948, in response to a wide demand for such a book, and a general desire to see the songs provided with English texts in addition to the original Norwegian text, Sons of Norway published a second printing of this book under the title of "SONS OF NORWAY SONG BOOK."

Carl G. O. Hansen, who was then the Editor of the Sons of Norway magazine, assisted by Frederick Wick, who was then the director in chief of the Norwegian Singers Association of America, and who had wide experience as a director, composer and music publisher, completed the monumental task of translating the Norwegian text of these beautiful Norwegian songs into English. The music was also rearranged for a great many of the songs so that it would serve as accompaniment to community singing, as well as providing music and text for singing by mixed choruses. Previously, this was not available for such universally beloved songs, such as: Reissiger's "Olaf Trygvason" and Grieg's "Landsighting," "Forward" and the "Sigurd Jorsalfar" ballads, which heretofore have been unobtainable in mixed chorus arrangements and with both the original and English texts. Essentially, the work of providing the English text was that of Mr. Hansen, and Mr. Wick served as adviser in musical matters.

Included in the collection were also the folk songs and some of the finest Norwegian ballads in arrangement for a solo voice with piano accompaniment. Now, in the year 1967, Sons of Norway again publishes for the third time, the Sons of Norway Song Book in its continuing effort to maintain and promote the best of our Norwegian culture, and, in this instance, through song.

The user of this new volume will find the mixed chorus arrangements always indicated by the initials S. A. T. B., which indicates the soprano, alto, tenor and bass. Not only is this helpful, but an incentive for groups of men and women to cultivate chorus singing.

Carl G. O. Hansen, in writing the previous preface in 1948, said: "Interest in the ballads which the immigrants have brought to this country has in late years been growing; hence there should be a place in American song literature for a volume which, as this one, contains a large selection of Norwegian songs arranged in an easily singable form and provided with English as well as the original Norwegian texts,"

We, who have come after, are proud to have had a part in contributing to the third printing of this beautiful volume.

Magne Smedvig

Sønner av Norge

O Sons of Norway

Sønner av Norge

2. Oldtid! du svant, men din hellige flamme
blusser i nordmannens hjerte ennu:
enn er av ætt og av kraft han den samme
enn står til frihet og ære hans hu;
Og når han kveder
Norriges heder
svulmer hans hjerte av stolthet og lyst;
ham er selv sydens de yndigste steder
intet mot Norriges snedekte kyst.

H. A. Bjerregård.

O Sons of Norway.

2. *Gone is that day, but its light blazes ever*
Holy and clear in each Norseman's brave heart;
Of the same race, the same strength and endeavor,
Freedom and right from his thoughts never part.
So when in writing,
Bravery citing,
Proud in his heart of old Norway's rich lore.
Joys of the Southlands are far less inviting
Than his own snow-covered, mountainous shore.

Olaf Morgan Norlie.

Sons of Old Norway.

Sons of old Norway assemble to cherish
All that is good which our forefathers gave.
Glories and memories that shall not perish
Give us the urge to be strong and be brave.
Here is our station,
In the new nation,
Here are our homes, here our future shall be.
Willingly, and with sincere adoration,
Give we our brawn to the land of the free.

Special English version by Carl G. O. Hansen.

The Star-Spangled Banner

FRANCIS SCOTT KEY S.A.T.B. JOHN STAFFORD SMITH

America

God Bless Our Native Land!

(Melody: America)

1. God bless our native land!
   Firm may she ever stand,
   Through storm and night,
   When the wild tempest rave,
   Ruler of wind and wave,
   Do Thou our country save
   By Thy great might!

2. For her our pray'rs shall rise
   To God above the skies,
   On Him we wait;
   Thou Who art ever nigh,
   Guarding with watchful eye,
   To Thee aloud we cry,
   God save the state!

Canadian National Hymn

1. God save our gracious King,
   Long live our noble King,
   God save the King:
   Send him victorious,
   Happy and glorious,
   Long to reign over us;
   God save the King.

2. Thy choicest gifts in store
   On him be pleased to pour;
   Long may he reign:
   May he defend our laws,
   And ever give us cause
   To sing with heart and voice
   God save the King.

Canadian stanza by the Rev. Robert Murray:

Our loved Dominion bless
With peace and happiness
From shore to shore;
And let our Empire be
United, loyal, free,
True to herself and Thee
For evermore.

O Canada

"That True North" (Tennyson)

S.A.T.B.

R. STANLEY WEIR, D.C.L.

C. LAVALLÉE

Maestoso

f

1. O Can - a - da! Our home and na - tive land! — True pa - triot
2. O Can - a - da! Where pines and ma - ples grow, — Great prai - ries
3. O Can - a - da! Be - neath thy shin - ing skies — May stal - wart

love in all thy sons com - mand. With glow - ing hearts we
spread and lord - ly riv - ers flow, How dear to us thy
sons and gen - tle maid - ens rise; To keep thee stead - fast

see thee rise The True North strong and free; And stand on guard, O
broad do - main, From East to West - ern sea! Thou land of hope for
through the years From East to West - ern sea. Our own be - lov - ed

Can - a - da, We stand on guard for thee.
all who toil! Thou True North strong and free!
na - tive land, Our True North strong and free.

CHORUS *ad lib.*

f

O Can - a - da! Glo - rious and free! We stand on guard, We stand on guard for thee.

ff *rit.*

O Can - a - da! We stand on guard for thee.

Ja, vi elsker dette landet

Yes, We Love This Land of Ours

2. Norske mann i hus og hytte,
takk din store Gud!
Landet vilde han beskytte,
skjønt det mørkt så ut
Alt, hvad fedrene har kjempet,
mødrene har grett,
:har den Herre stille lempet,
så vi vant vår rett.:

Bj. Bjornson.

2. Norsemen, in whatever station,
Thank your mighty God;
He has kindly saved our nation
From oppression's rod.
That for which our sires contended
And our mothers wailed,
Silently the Lord defended,
So our rights, our rights prevailed.:

O.O. Lien.

Du gamla, du fria

O, Glorious Land of the North

S. A. T. B.

Swedish and English Text.

SWEDISH NATIONAL ANTHEM
A Folk Song
Arr. by F. W.

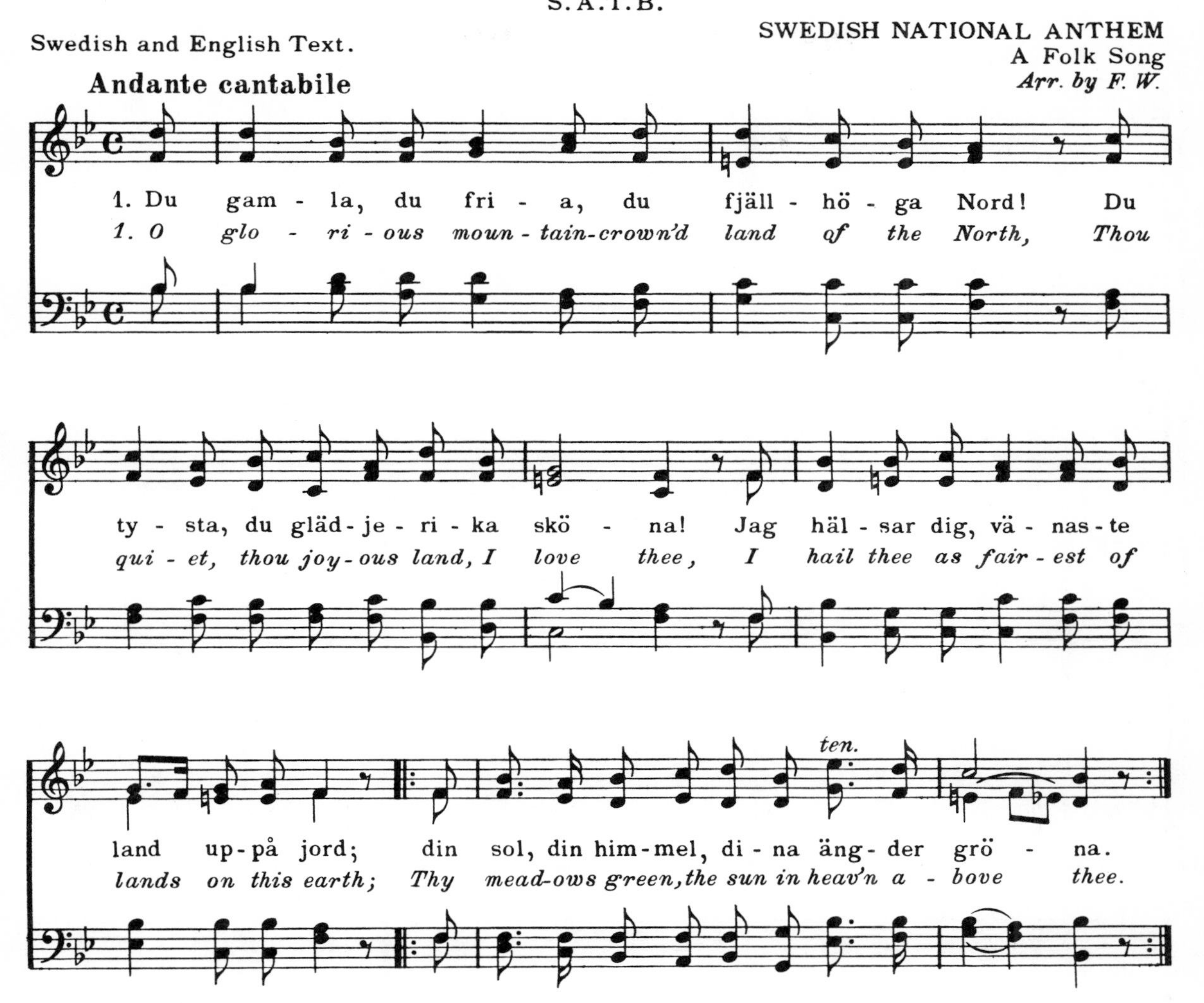

2. Du tronar på minnen från fornstora dar,
Då ärat ditt namn flög över jorden.
Jag vet, att du är och du blir hvad du var;
Ja, jag vill leva, jag vill dö i Norden,
Ja, jag vill leva, jag vill dö i Norden.

2. Thy throne is the mem'ry of great days of yore,
When all through the world thy name was carried,
Thou art this, I know, the same as of old.
In thee I'll live, in thee I'll die, thou North Land,
In thee I live, in thee I'll die, thou North Land.

Der er et yndigt Land

There is a Beauteous Land

S.A.T.B.

E. KRÖYER
Danish National Anthem

2. Det Land endnu er skjönt;
thi blaa sig Söen belter,
og Lövet staar saa grönt,
og Lövet staar saa grönt.
Og ædle Kvinder, skjönne Möer
og Mænd og raske Svende
bebo de Danskes Öer,
bebo de Danskes Öer.

Adam Oehlenschläger.

2. Its beauty still is seen.
The blue sea has it girdled.
The leafage stands so green,
The leafage stands so green.
And noble women, maidens fair,
And men, and sturdy laddies
Dwell on the Danes' old Isles,
Dwell on the Danes' old Isles.

Carl G. O. Hansen.

Vårt Land

Our Native Land

S.A.T.B.

F. PACIUS
Finnish National Anthem

2. Vårt land är fattigt, skall så bli
for den, som gull begär.
En främling far oss stolt forbi;
men detta landet älska vi.
För oss med moar, fjäll och skär
et gull-land dock det är.

J. L. Runneberg.

2. Our land is poor; and shall be, too,
For those who gold desire;
Proud strangers look at us askew,
But we, we love this land, we do —
To us, our cliffs, and fields, and mire,
Are gold for son and sire.

O.M. Norlie.

Vi er et Folk

A People We

GRETRY

2. Hvor nordmenn før i verden fant
et land der godt ham huet,
for det hans blod så ofte rant
og ingen makt ham kuet.
På Englands jord, på Irlands kyst
han vågede så mangen dyst,
han Nordmandi i fred fikk lyst,
mens rundt omkring det truet.

3. Vi er det største vikingkull
som tusenåret fødte
vi strøk da stuen blev for full,
mor ingen fra sig støtte.
Den slektens arv som vi tok med
den odlet var i krig og fred,
i hungerår, ved tro, ved sved,
da Eidsvoldtinget møtte.

4. Ja, måtte vi i språk og tro
ved neste sekel møtes,
og måtte norskhet stetse gro
og nordmenns hjerter glødes
så Haralds tanke, Olavs sak,
må bære vårt og Norges flag,
så utav Eidsvoldsminnets dag
til større dåd vi fødes.

Knud Wefald.

2. Where'er before the Norseman found
A country to his liking,
His blood he'd give to hold the ground,
The ever valiant Viking.
On England's soil, on Irish strand,
He often boldly took his stand,
Made Normandy a peaceful land
While foemen fiercely threatened.

3. We are the largest Viking band
In thousand years appearing.
Of own free will we left a land
And scenes that were endearing.
And on our way, that we be strong,
A heritage we brought along
In courage, hero deeds and song
Forever here to cherish.

4. As Sons of Norway here we stand
In ranks of firm formation,
Prepared to guard, defend the land,
The welfare of the nation.
Let's give our strength and give our deed
Relieving suffering and need.
Til Dovre falls, this is our creed:
Keep faith without cessation!

Carl G.O. Hansen

Det er min sjel en frydfull trang

(Mel: "Vi er et folk")

1. Det er min sjel en frydfull trang
   å gjeste Norges dale.
   Den gamle fjellkoll elsker sang,
   de glade hjerters tale.
   Kom til den fagre Maridal!
   til Kleivens svimlende portal!
   kom hvorsomhelst og Norge skal
   dig i sin favn husvale.

2. Hist slanken selje hegg og pil
   og rogn isammenranke.
   De nøkne fjell de dekke vil,
   det er en kjærlig tanke.
   Så norske brødre, bryst ved bryst,
   vi ville med vemodig lyst
   vår moders brøst selv hylle til.
   Det er en kjærlig tanke.

Henrik Wergeland.

Within My Soul There Is An Urge

(Mel: "Vi er et folk")

1. *Within my soul there is an urge*
   To visit Norway's valleys.
   The mountains old with music surge
   And happy heart-throb tallies.
   See Maridal in all her prime,
   View Kleiven's dizzy height sublime!
   Go anywhere at any time,
   Her beauty Norway rallies.

2. *The slender willow, spruce and pine,*
   To shield the mountains bareness,
   Their foliage they intertwine;
   A thought of tender fairness.
   Thus, good Norse brothers, hand in hand,
   We join and fondly take our stand
   Our mother's failings to confine.
   A thought of tender fairness.

Carl G. O. Hansen

The Sturdy Norseman

(Melody: "Vi er et folk")

1. The sturdy Norseman's home of yore
   Was on the foaming wave.
   And there he gathered bright renown,
   The bravest of the brave.
   Oh, ne'er should we forget our sires,
   Wher'ever we may be;
   They bravely won a gallant name,
   And ruled the stormy sea.

2. And let us well remember now
   How it was wont to be,
   When boldly forth the vikings sailed,
   And conquered Normandie.
   We still may sing their deeds of fame,
   In thrill harmony;
   For they did win a gallant name,
   And ruled the stormy sea.

3. Oh, Norway, mother of the brave,
   We greet thee now with pleasure!
   Success and freedom sweet you gave
   Your sons in fullest measure.
   Old Dovre mingles with our glee,
   And joins our shouts with "three times three."
   Oh, Norway, mother of the brave,
   We greet thee now with pleasure!

Sons of Norway

(Music page 10 Sons of Norway Song Book)

We welcome you to this our home
of brotherhood and pleasure.
We bid you join us and become
our friends in greatest measure.
We welcome you and raise our voice;
in happiness we now rejoice.
Our chain is strengthened by your choice
to aid our Lodge and Order.

We give a helping hand to all
our sick and needy members.
We make our fellowship recall
the ties that bind forever.
The sacred trust we have received;
and founding fathers had achieved
A brotherhood to fill the need
of Norway's sons and daughters.

The saga tells of many deeds
by Norsemen brave and hardy;
of venturing across the seas
in quest of freedom's bounty.
On western shores they made their stand;
of us these hero deeds demand
a true allegiance to this land
and honor to the Norsemen.

Be with us in our work and play;
know our Fraternal Order.
Be kind and helpful day by day;
be friends with one another.
Let freedom always be our aim
and progress comes and will remain
As long as our fraternal chain
will strengthen Sons of Norway.

E. B. Hauke

Fremad! Fremad!

Forward

EDV. GRIEG

2. "Fremad, Fremad!"
hver som elsker frie hjem,
"Fremad, Fremad!"
friheten må evig frem.
Skal den også prøves
i tvil og nederlag,
hvem teller vel de tapte slag
på seirens dag?

3. "Fremad, Fremad!"
hver som fast på folket tror,
"Fremad, Fremad!"
hver som søker fedres spor.
Nordens ånd har skatte,
forgjemt i fjellets ly,
de finnes må i morgengry
og frem pàny.

Bj. Bjørnson.

2. "Forward, Forward!"
Whoso loves a home that's free,
"Forward, Forward!"
Freedom's course must ever be.
Though it shall be tested
By doubt and by defeat,
Who will the losses' count repeat
When vict'ries greet?

3. "Forward, Forward!"
Whoso trusts in Norway's day.
"Forward, Forward!"
Whoso goes our fathers' way.
Hid in northern mountains
Are spirit-treasures true
They shall, when dawns the morning's blue,
Come forth anew.

A. H. Palmer.

En sangers bønn

A Singer's Prayer

2. La min sangerkrans da slynges
hen i støv på glemsels kyst,
når kun hist hvor alt forynges
sjelens dyp har lutret røst;
når kun der jeg griper tonen
i dét store kvad for tronen,
som til himlens harper synges.

J. S. Welhaven.

2. Let the songs of my creation
Waste in dust on oblivion's shore,
If in yon rejuvenation
Purer tones my soul adore,
If but there my voice is blending
With the choir all transcending
In the celestial jubilation.

Carl G.O.Hansen.

Norge, Norge!

Norway, Norway!

KRISTIAN WENDELBORG

2. Norge, Norge!
skibakkeløpets skinnende land,
sjøulkens havn og fiskeleie,
fløterens veie,
gjeterens fjell-ljom og jøkelbrand.
Akre, enge, runer i skoglandet,
spredte skår,
byer som blomster,
elvene skyter ut hvor det bryter
hvitt ifra havet hvor svermen går.
Norge, Norge! Hytter og hus
og ingen borge, blidt eller hårdt,
du er vårt, du er vårt,
du er fremtidens land.

Bj. Bjørnson.

2. *Norway, Norway!*
Glistening heights where skees swiftly go,
Harbors with fishermen, salts, and craftsmen,
Rivers and raftsmen,
Herdsmen and horns and the glacier-glow,
Moors and meadows,
Runes in the woodlands, and wide-mown swaths,
Cities like flowers, streams that run dashing
Out to the flashing
White of the sea, where the fish-school froths.
Norway, Norway! Houses and huts,
No castles grand, gentle or hard,
Thee we guard, thee we guard,
Thee our future's fair land.

A.H. Palmer.

Barndomsminne frå Nordland

The Lands of My Love

2. Denne heim er meg kjær som den beste på jord.
Han mitt hjarta er nær, denne fjetrande fjord,
og det målande fjell og den strålande kveld,
hugen leikar, den leikar på deim,
å eg minnest, å eg minnest,
å eg minnest so væl denne heim.

Elias Blix.

To America:

Here's a land of great beauty so vast and so wide,
Where millions found refuge and now abide.
Here does liberty sway and progress has play.
'Tis the land of my Star Spangled pride.
: And I love it, yes I love it,
Yes I love it because it is mine. :

Carl G. O. Hansen.

Sølvet

Silver

Venetiansk serenade

Venetian Serenade

2. Ei din kappe med du tage,
sommernatten er så varm;
kun ditt lette slør du slynger
om ditt hår, din hals og barm.
Kom, Carina, ved måneskjær!
Kom, Bellina, oss ingen ser.

3. I min arm du skal ei fryse
i den tause midnattsstund;
sløret glider fra din skulder,
og jeg kysser hals og munn.
Kom, Carina, ved måneskjær!
Kom, Bellina, oss ingen ser.

2. You'll not need, love, your mantilla,
Summer nights like these are warm;
Wrap your veil of white about you,
It will shield you well from harm.
Come, Carina, the moon is bright!
Come, Bellina, how fair the night!

3. In my arms I'll fondly hold you,
While the silent midnight flies;
Tenderly, in love, enfold you,
And I'll kiss your lips and eyes.
Come, Carina, the moon is bright!
Come, Bellina, how fair the night!

★In Italian "Carina" means my dear one, and "Bellina" means my fair one.

Siste reis

The Sailor's Last Voyage

Norwegian by Henrik Wergeland
English by Carl G.O. Hansen

EYVIND ALNÆS

Med stran - de av de - mant og gull,
Like gold and diamonds all a - round,
rit. e dim.
rit.
a tempo
sing, sail - or, oh, er him - lens hav av ø - er full, sing, sail - or, oh. Det
sing, sail - or, oh, The heav - en sea with isles a - bound, sing, sail - or, oh, They
p
mp
er de stjer - ner, kla - re, små, sing, sail - or, oh, som du på nat - te - vak - ten så,
are the stars so small and clear, sing, sail - or, oh, At which, as night - watch, you would peer,
p a tempo
sing, sail - or, oh!
sing, sail - or, oh!
mf
dim. e rit.

Maestoso
f
ff
f a tempo
Frisk an da, mo - dig til la stå, sing, sail - or, oh, i - gjen - nem sky opp
Take cour - age then and risk de - fy, sing, sail - or, oh, While sail - ing up through
Maestoso
f
ff
f a tempo
8
i det blå, sing, sail - or, oh. Frykt ei for dje - ve - lens kor - sar.
az - ure sky, sing, sail - or, oh. Fear not the dev - il's fierce cor - sairs,
ff rit.
f a tempo
mf rit.
sing, sail - or, oh, du går ham gan - ske sik - kert klar, sing, sail - or,
sing, sail - or, oh, No dan - ger of his wil - y snares, sing, sail - or,
ff
f a tempo
mf rit.
oh.
oh.
p
mf
rit.
p

p dolce
rit.
lento
a tempo
Du møter viv, du møter venn, sing, sail - or, oh, du
You'll meet your wife, you'll meet your friend, sing, sail - or, oh, Your
møter dine barn igjen, sing, sail - or, oh. Da
children you will meet again, sing, sail - or, oh. Then
pp
mf
bry - ter stør - re gle - der løs, sing, sail - or,
there will be much great - er glee, sing, sail - or,
lento
ten.
oh, enn når du her kom hjem fra sjøs, sing, sail - or, oh.
oh, Than here when you came home from sea, sing sail - or oh.

Lengsel

Longing

HALFDAN KJERULF

2. Min tanke jeg dig sendte,
jeg sendte dig mitt blikk.
Ak, hvor mitt hjerte brente
at intet svar jeg fikk:
kun pust fra nattevinden,
fra grenen hist et vink,
den kolde dug
fra linden, fra linden
og stjernens kolde blikk.

3. Du tenker vel jeg har glemt dig,
men tro mig, om du kan,
jeg har i hjertet gjemt dig
og skal over gravens rand,
tross dødens bitre kulde,
hinsides livets kyst
bære ditt navn
det hulde, det hulde,
prentet dypt i mitt bryst

2. I think of you in the daytime,
I dream of you by night;
One word from your lips, my darling,
Would flood my soul with light.
A murmuring low, in the wildwood,
Responds alone from afar,
As cold as the dew
On the leaves of the linden,
Ah! cold as yon distant star.

3. O think not I can forget you,
I could not, if I would;
Deep in my heart lies hidden
Your image, pure and good.
Tho' sorrow and care may oppress me
I'll strive for a goal above;
Thro' life and in death
You'll be with me, my darling,
Enshrin'd in my heart's best love.

Seterjentens søndag

The Chalet Girl's Sunday

2. Det nytter ei stort å tage sin bok
og synge i heien sin salme;
mitt loft er for høit, og her er det dog
som tonene blekne og falme.
O den som idag fikk blande sin røst
med hans og de øvriges stemme!
Gud give at snart det lakket mot høst,
Gud give jeg atter var hjemme!

Jørgen Moe.

2. To open one's book 'tis useless to try,
And psalms out of doors begin singing;
So distant my loft, 'twould seem, here on high
That tones become poor while they're ringing.
Ah, happy the one whose voice could in song
With his and the others be blending!
God grant that the harvest come before long,
My flock and myself homeward sending.

Auber Forestier.

Synnøves sang

Synnøve's Song

H. KJERULF

2. Jeg tenkte, leken den skulde gå
ut fra de løvede, lyse birke,
dit frem hvor Solbakkehuse stå
og til den rødmalte kirke.

3. Jeg satt og ventet såmangen kveld
og så dit bort under graneheien;
men skygget gjorde det mørke fjell,
og du, du fant ikke veien.

Bj. Björnson.

2. I thought that play would go on for aye,
From bowers leading of leafy birches
To where Solbakke houses lay,
And where the red-painted church is.

3. I sat and waited through evenings long
And scanned the ridge with the spruces yonder;
But darkening mountains made shadows throng,
And you the way did not wander.

A. H. Palmer.

Ingrids vise

Ingrid's Song

Norwegian by Bj. Bjørnson
English by A.H. Palmer

HALFDAN KJERULF

2. Og reven lo under birkerot
bortved lynget, bortved lynget.
Og haren hoppede i ville mot
over lynget, over lynget.
Jeg er så glad over alle ting!
Hu-hei, gjør du slike svære spring
over lynget, over lynget? La, la, la, la, la!

3. Og reven ventet bak birkerot
bortved lynget, bortved lynget.
Og haren tumlede ham midt imot
over lynget, over lynget.
Men Gud forbarme sig, er du der!
—Aa, kjære, hvor tør du danse her
over lynget, over lynget? La, la, la, la, la!

2. The fox laughed low by the birch tree's root
In the heather, in the heather.
The hare was running with daring foot
O'er the heather, o'er the heather
I am so happy for everything!
Hallo! Why go you with mighty spring
O'er the heather, o'er the heather? La, etc.

3. The fox lay hid by the birch tree's root
In the heather, in the heather.
The hare dashed to him with reckless foot
O'er the heather, o'er the heather.
May God have mercy, but this is queer!
Good gracious, how dare you dance so here
O'er the heather, o'er the heather? La, etc.

Jeg lengter mot sol og sommer

I'm Longing for Sunlight and Summer

2. Jeg lengter dit jøkler luer
og glitrer i solfallsglans,
hvor stormen en høstnatt treder
på fjellet sin ville dans.
Jeg lengter dit bølgen leker
langs leden blandt siv og tang
og nynner i månenetter
sin selsomme, såre sang.

3. O Norge, din granskogs sødme
engang å få ånde inn!
Få lytte til huldrens sanger
på vidden en vårnatt linn!
O, ennu engang, mor Norge,
å skue ditt skyblå hav!
Få dølge min såre lengsel
og takke for alt du gav!

Robert Jæger Loennecken.

2. I long to the blazing glaciers
That glitter in sunset glow,
To hills where in nights autumnal
The furious tempests blow.
I long to where wavelets playing
On channel and sedgy shore
Are humming in silver moonlight
Their mystical song of yore.

3. O Norway, to breathe the sweetness
Again of thy greenwoods bright
And listen to fairies singing
On moorlands a summer night!
O, once more, thou ageless mother,
To gaze at thy skyblue wave,
To silence my heartsore longing,
And thank you for all you gave.

A. Faurschou.

Norge i rødt, hvitt og blått

Norway in Red White and Blue

(On the Liberation of Norway in 1945)

Norwegian by Finn Bø
English by Carl G.O. Hansen

LARS-ERIK LARSSON

1. Hvor hen du går i li og fjell en vin - ter - dag, en som - mer - kveld, ved
1. Wher - e'er o'er rocks and rills you roam, In win - ter or in sum - mer gloam, Or

fjord og fos - se - vell, fra eng og mo med fu - ru - trær, fra
where the wa - ters foam, From mead - ows and the tow'r - ing pines, From

ha - vets bryn med fis - ke - vær og til de hvi - te skjær,
sea - shore and the fish - con - fines, Out to the sker - ry lines,

mø - ter du lan - det i tre - far - vet drakt svøpt i et gjen - skinn av
View you the land in the three col - ors deck'd, Col - ors from our flag their

flag - gets far - ve - prakt. Se, en hvit - stam - met bjerk opp - i hei - en ram - mer
ra - di - ance re - flect. In the hill - sides the white, slen - der birch - es seem the

stri - pen av blå - klok - ker inn mot den rød - mal - te stu - en ved
patch - es of blue - bells to seize, At the road - side a red cot - tage

2. En vårdag i en solskinstund
på benken i studenterlund'
der sitter han og hun,
to unge, nyutsprungne russ,
to ganske nylig tente bluss
i tyve grader pluss.
Hun er som en gryende forsommerdag,
som farves av gjenskinnet fra det norske flagg.
Ja, så hvit som det hvite er kjolen
og sa rødt som det rø' hennes kinn,
hennes øyne er blå som fiolen,
hun er flagget som vaier i vind.
Han har freidig og hvitlugget panne
og en lue i rødt har han fått.
Med en lysebla tiltro til landet,
står vår ungdom i rødt, hvitt og blått.

3. De kjempet både hun og han!
Nå lyser seirens baunebrann
ut over Norges land.
Mot himlen stiger flagg ved flagg
som tusen gledesbål idag
for alle vunne slag.
Det knitrer som før over hytte og slott
et flammende merke i rødt og hvitt og blått.
Som et regnbuens tegn under skyen
skal det evig i fremtiden stå.
Se, det glitrer igjen over byen
i det røde og hvite og blå!
La det runge fra gaten og torget,
over landet som nordmenn har fått:
Du er vårt, du er vårt, gamle Norge!
Vi vil kle deg i rødt, hvitt og blått.

2. 'Tis spring, the sun is shining bright,
On bench beneath a shady tree
Are seated he and she.
They're freshies both and full of hope
With vars'ty studies they will cope
And give life greater scope.
She seems like the dawn of the day summertime,
Reflecting the Norwegian colors sublime.
Yes, as fair as the white of her dress is,
And the red like her ruddy cheeks' glow,
Her blue eyes just the vi'let's blue stresses;
She's the flag flown in breezes that blow.
His an open and white-tousled forehead
And a cap that is red★ came his due.
Such firm faith in their fatherland's shore had
These our youths in the red, white and blue.

3. And fight did they both she and he!
So blaze the fires of victory
For now is Norway free!
And skyward up the flags are run
Like thousand joy salutes of gun
For all the battles won.
O'er castle and cottage there crackles anew
The flaming insigne in red and white and blue.
Like a rainbow 'neath sky as a token
Stands for now and eternity, too,
With its glistening ever unbroken
In the red and the white and the blue.
Then resounding from street and from doorway
O'er the land that was given to you:
This is our, this is our good, old Norway!
We will dress you in red, white and blue!

★Red is the color of the university freshman cap.

Hils fra mig der hjemme

A Sailor's Greeting

English Version by F. Wick

REFRAIN
p-f
Hils fra mig der hjem - me, hils min far og mor,
Greet my dear, old moth - er, Greet my fa - ther too
hils de grøn - ne li - er, og den blan - ke fjord.
And my lit - tle broth - er When he wel - comes you.
Hvis jeg had - de vin - ger fløi jeg hjem med dig, til de
Had I wings to fol - low Hap - py would I be Dear - est
ly - se net - ter. Hils dem! Hils fra mig! mig!
lit - tle swal - low, Greet them all from me. me.
1
2

Mens Nordhavet bruser

Norway's Flag

IBSEN

2. Du blomster av palmen på frihets grunn,
skjøn er du å skue trefarvet;
det hvitene kors i den røde bunn,
det har du av Danebrog arvet;
men hjertebladet, det mørkeblå,
av frihets marg måtte først utgå.

3. Fra himlen falt Danebrogsfanen ned,
blev tvillinglandsnekkernes smykke
og stod gjennem sekler i krig og fred,
omstrålet af heder og lykke.
O, flagg for Norrig, stand evig så,
mist aldri ditt hjerteblads høie blå!

C. N. Schwach.

2. Thou flow'r of the palm, on the free soil found,
Tri-colored and beautiful flower!
The cross there of white on the blood red ground
From Danebrog that was thy dower;
The heart's own leaf, though, of dusky blue,
From freedom's marrow first it grew.

3. From Heaven the Danebrog flag fell down,
Thro' ages the twin nations' glory;
In war and in peace 'twas the dragon's crown,
Aglow with good fortune in story,
O Norway's flag, to thyself be true,
Nor lose thy heart-leaf of dusky blue.

Auber Forestier.

Blandt alle lande

Of All the Lands

Norwegian by Ole Vig
English by R.B. Anderson

H.M. HANSEN

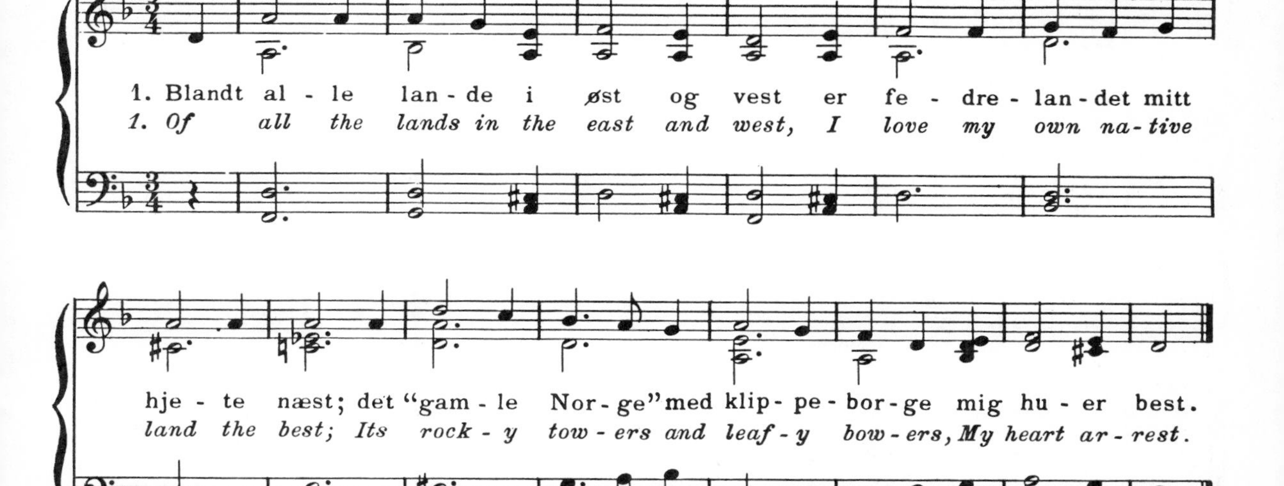

2. Fra Vesterhavet til Kjølens rand,
fra Nordishavet til Kristiansand,
der har jeg hjemme
og kan istemme:
mitt fedreland.

3. Jeg elsker eder, I gamle fjell,
med høie tinder og dybe vell,
med skog om barmen
og jern i armen
til tidens kveld.

4. Jeg elsker eder, I bekker små,
I stolte fosser, I fjorder blå,
I sjøer blanke
hvis stille tanke
kan stjerner nå.

2. From Sweden's border to North Sea strand,
From Artic ocean to Christiansand,
My home I name it,
In song proclaim it,
My native land.

3. Its yawning gorges I love so well,
Mid peaks and snow-crested citadel,
With woods abounding,
With iron resounding,
Till time's last knell.

4. I love the murmuring brooklet shy,
The blue-tinged fjords and forces high,
The lakelets blinking,
Their deep thoughts sinking
To starlit sky.

Nyss seilet vi en solblank time

In Merry Sunshine We Came Sailing

Norwegian: L. Dietrichson
English: Carl G.O. Hansen

F. ABT

Hill dig, du gamle land

Hail to the Old Homeland

SVEN ULSAKER

2. Hill dig, vårt unge folk
med dine gamle minner:
hjemfarne slekters tolk,
som taler fra li og tinder.
Folkets dåd i nutids kamp
fremtid med fortid binder.
Gud signe Norges folk,
Gud signe Norges minner!

Sven Ulsaker.

2. Hail ye, our people young
With memories of glory!
Cherish forefathers' deeds
Related in song and story.
Deeds performed in our day's strife,
Link with the past the future.
God bless all Norway's life!
God bless the precious mem'ries!

Carl G. O. Hansen.

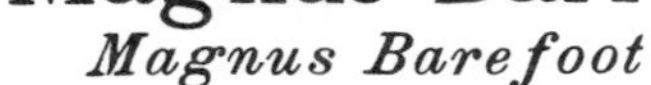

Magnus Barfot*

Magnus Barefoot

B. CRUSELL

* Magnus Barfot, a warlike king of Norway, who was given his sobriquet because he adopted the Scotch fighters' dress; he perished in a battle with the Irish in 1103.

2. Jeg fremmest gikk pa blodig val
ei enset sår.
Til æren konger beile skal,
men ei til år.

3. Som løven kjæmper mot en skokk
av mindre dyr,
så kjæmpet jeg mot tallrik flokk
i irske myr.

4. Der segnet jeg blandt lik og blod
i mudret grav;
men navnet mitt en vinge god
dog saga gav.

H. Heyerdahl.

2. On bloody field my lead was stern,
For wounds no fears.
For honor ev'ry king should yearn,
And not for years.

3. As fights the lion smaller beasts:
Though task was harsh,
I fought a horde of fiercest foes
In Irish marsh.

4. There perished I 'mongst bones and blood
In boggy grave;
But my proud name a wing so good
The Saga gave.

Carl G. O. Hansen.

Det stig av hav eit Alveland

1. Det stig av hav eit Alveland
med tind og mo;
det kviler klårt mot himmelrand
i kveldblå ro.

2. Eg såg det tidt som sveipt i eim
bak havdis grå;
det er ein huld, ein heilag heim,
me ei kan nå.

3. Når dagen sig som eld og blod
i blåe-myr,
det logar op med glim og glo
og æventyr.

4. Men av han døyr, den bleike brand,
som slokna glo,
og klart som fyrr ligg Alveland
i kveldblå ro.

5. Eg lengtar tidt på trøytte veg
der ut til fred;
men landet fyrst kan syna seg,
når sol gjeng ned.

Arne Garborg.

A Fairyland

1. A fairyland it seems to be
With peak and plain,
A spot enchanted out at sea,
Where peace doth reign.

2. I saw it oft, this hazy dome
Off ocean beach.
It is a beauteous sacred home
I cannot reach.

3. When day descends like blood and fire
In blue deep vale,
It looms up like flaming spire —
A fairytale.

4. It pales and dies, the smold'ring brand,
Just embers few,
And clear as before lies Fairyland
In evening's blue.

5. I often long, on weary way,
For peace out yon.
The land, only then, see I may
When sun goes down.

Carl G. O. Hansen.

Skjønn er våren i vårt Norges dale

2. Skjønnest dog av alt er ånde-våren,
frihets frembrudd hos et edelt folk.
I dens glans se Nor, av Gud udkåren
til å vorde store tankers tolk!
Frihets-solen løste vintrens lenker,
signet hver en vrå med liv og lyst;
himlen overalt sin fylde senker,
og av dådskraft svulmer hvert et bryst.

M. J. Monrad.

2. Grand above all else is spirit's springtime,
Freedom's birth the people has aroused.
Thus to Norway fate the task has given
Great and noble thoughts to be espoused.
Freedom's sun released the chains of winter,
Gave unto each nook its life and zest;
Heaven over all its plenty yielding,
Will to do and dare in ev'ry breast.

Carl G.O. Hansen.

Eg elskar dei voggande tonar

I Love Every Tune

CHR. LEPSOE

2. Og den som med mod sig vende
mot det som var vandt å nå.
Og hjarta som sorgi kjende,
og endå, endå kan soli sjå,
og hjarta som sorgi kjende,
og endå, endå kan soli sjå.

3. Eg elskar livet som strøymer
med voner i unge barm,
eg elskar livet som gløymer
all livsens, livsens sut og harm,
eg elskar livet som gløymer
all livsens, livsens sut og harm.

2. *The courage that's bent on pursuing*
Whatever is good and bold,
The heart which in grief is ruing
And still can sunshine, sunshine behold,
The heart which in grief is ruing
And still can sunshine, sunshine behold.

3. *I love all in life that's begetting*
Fond hopes in the youthful mind;
I love the life when forgetting
Its woes, its acts and words unkind,
I love the life when forgetting
Its woes, its acts and words unkind.

Carl G.O. Hansen.

Kan du glemme gamle Norge?

Old Norway

2. Kan du glemme dette landet
som dig først tok i sin favn?
Mon du finne vil et annet
med så stolt og herlig navn?

3. Kan du glemme Norges skover
med sin furu, birk og gran?
Kan du glemme sjøens vover,
alt du da forglemme kan.

4. Kan du glemme disse trange
fjorde, som sig bukter inn?
Hvor som barn du mange gange
vugget dig for førlig vind?

5. Svever stundom ei din tanke
dithen hvor din vugge stod?
Føler du ei hjertet banke
for det land som du forlot?

6. La da kun din tanke sveve;
det kan aldri falle tungt.
Må for nordmenn lenge leve
gamle Norge, evig ungt!

2. How can you forget old Norway,
Land of everlasting fame?
: Can you ever find another
With so glorious a name? :

3. How can you forget old Norway
And its narrow fjords so grand,
: In and out between the mountains?
'Tis my own, my native land. :

Serenade

WOMEN'S VOICES

(English and Norwegian Text)

English Version by
Wilhelm Pettersen

KJERULF

Halfdan Kjerulf (Pronounced Chairulf) was born Sept. 15, 1815, in Oslo, Norway. As a young man he began the study of law, but finally devoted himself wholly to music. His compositions are characterized by a smooth, flowing and noble melody, are original in conception, full of warmth and delicacy, and exceedingly finished in style. Some of his works, like "The Bridal Party at Hardanger" and "Last Night" became universal favorites. He died August 11, 1868, at Grefsen Baths near Oslo.

tril - ler, dug - gens per - ler tril - ler, må - nens strå - ler spil - ler
ti - er, sukk og kla - ge ti - er, vin - dens pust be - fri - er
shin - ing bright, When the stars are shin - ing bright, Up a - bove at mid - night,
ring - ing, Dis - tant bells are ring - ing; Gen - tle breez - es wing - ing,
tril - ler, dug - gens per - ler tril - ler, må - nens strå - ler spil - ler
ti - er, sukk og kla - ge ti - er, vin - dens pust be - fri - er
shin - ing bright, When the stars are shin - ing bright, Up a - bove at mid - night,
ring - ing, Dis - tant bells are ring - ing; Gen - tle breez - es wing - ing,
tril - ler, dug - gens per - ler tril - ler, må - nens strå - ler spil - ler
ti - er, sukk og kla - ge ti - er, vin - dens pust be - fri - er
shin - ing bright, When the stars are shin - ing bright, Up a - bove at mid - night,
ring - ing, Dis - tant bells are ring - ing; Gen - tle breez - es wing - ing,
dim. e rit.
ppp
hen - ad sjø - ens glar, hen - ad, hen - ad, sjø - ens glar.
det be - tyng - te sinn, det be - tyng - te sinn.
Still - ness ev - 'ry - where, Still - ness, Still - ness ev - 'ry - where.
All com - plaints a - way, All com - plaints a - way a - way.
ppp
hen - ad sjø - ens glar, hen - ad, hen - ad, hen - ad sjø - ens glar.
det be - tyng - te sinn, det be - tyng - te, det be - tyng - te sinn.
Still - ness ev - 'ry - where, Still - ness, Still - ness, Still - ness ev - 'ry - where.
All com - plaints a - way, All com - plaints, All com - plaints a - way.
ppp
hen - ad sjø - ens glar, hen - ad, hen - ad, hen - ad sjø - ens glar.
det be - tyng - te sinn, det be - tyng - te, det be - tyng - te sinn.
Still - ness ev - 'ry - where, ev - 'ry - where, Still - ness, Still - ness ev - 'ry - where
All com - plaints a - way, all com - plaints, All, All com - plaints a - way.
dim. e rit.
ppp

Vi vil oss et land

mf
ten.
Nor - ge. Og har vi ik - ke det land en - nu, så
Nor - way. And have we not this our land for aye, Then
ten.
mf
ten.
skal vi vin - ne det, jeg og du! Og har vi ik - ke det land en - nu, så
we shall win it, yes, you and I! And have we not this our land for aye, Then
ten.
Tempo I
rit.
f
skal vi vin - ne det, jeg og du! Vi vil oss et land som er
we shall win it, yes, you and I! We want this fair land to be
f
Tempo I
rit.
f

Norge, mitt Norge!

Norway, My Norway

S.A.T.B.

Norwegian by Theodor Caspari
English by O.T. Arneson

ALFRED PAULSEN
Arr. by Frederick Wick

Andante tranquillo

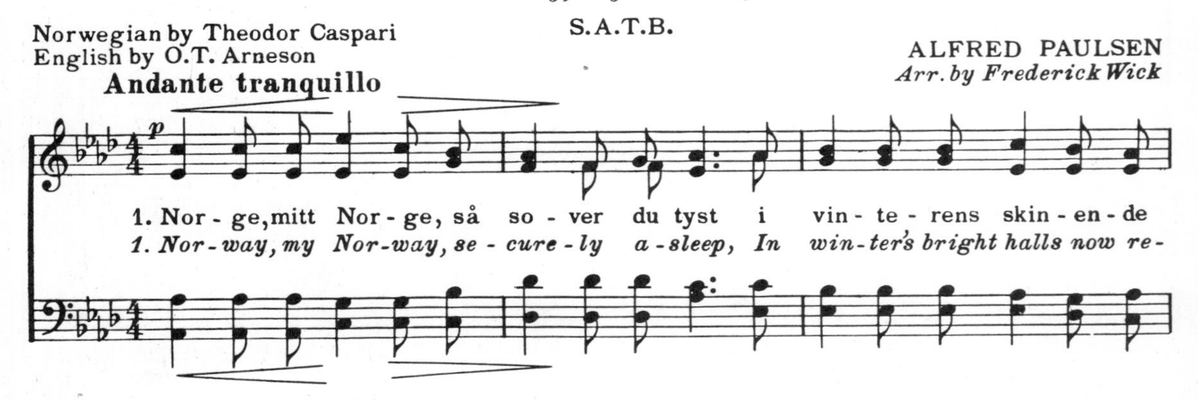

2. Norge, mitt Norge! så giv mig din vår
med sol over vuggende vanne.
Men hør mig, ja, hør mig: når dagen forgår
og aftenen skygger min panne,
da lær mig å visne, å Norge, min mor!
og red mig en seng i din hellige jord,
når sommeren drager av lande.

2. Norway, my Norway! let springtime appear
With sunshine and warmth for the meadows;
But hear me, oh, hear me: when evening draws near,
With coolness and lengthening shadows.
Oh Norway! Then teach me to wither and die,
And grant in your hallowed ground I may lie,
When summer and life are departing.

Landkjenning

Landsighting

S.A.T.B.

Norwegian by Bj. Bjørnson
English by Carl G.O. Hansen

EDVARD GRIEG

fz
fp
det-te for mur i hav - bry-net?"
tow-er-ing wall o'er sea loom-ing?"
sf
ff
p
cresc.
mf
f
Og det var O-laf Tryg-va-son, lan-det syn-tes gan-ske stengt,— al-le hans un-ge
And it was O-laf Tryg-va-son, Closed the land ap-pear'd to all — Seem'd as his youth-ful
cresc.
kon - ge-leng-sler føl-tes mot klip-pen sprengt, inn-til en skald op-da - get hvi-te
king - ly long-ings shat-tered 'gainst moun-tain wall, Then did a skald dis-cov - er spires and
marc.

kup-ler og spir i sky - la-get
tow-er-ing domes midst clouds hov-er
fp
fp
dim.
ten.
p
COR.
p
TROM.
pp
pp
Og det var O - laf Tryg - va-son
And it was O - laf Tryg - va-son,
pp
pp
pp

cresc.
syn - tes han - med en - gang så
Loom'd at once be - fore his sight
cresc.
cresc.
mf
grå - spreng - te, gam - le tem - pel mu - re
Walls of a hoar - y an - cient tem - ple
mf
mf
cresc.
sne - hvi - te hvelv der på,
Vault - ed by arch - es white,
cresc.
cresc.

f
leng - tes han da så så - re, med sin
Yearned he to be with - in it, For his
ten.
Ped.
un - ge tro stå in - nen -
glo - ri - ous faith for - ev - er
cresc.
fo - re.
win it.
cresc. molto

Maestoso
ff
Lan - det sig åp - ned, vår det var
Spring-time and sun-light deck'd the land,
ff
Maestoso
ff
Ped. * Ped. * Ped. * Ped. *
du - ren - de av fos - se - brus,
Wa-ters wild-ly rush'd and roar'd
storm - vær og hav - dønn
Rag - ing were storms, the
Ped. * Ped. * Ped. * Ped. * Ped. *
rundt om - kring dem, sæl - som var sko - gens sus.
o - cean surg - ing, strange was the syl - van chord.
poco rit.
Ped. * Ped. * Ped. * Ped. * Ped. *

Molto più lento
Kon - gen hen-før - tes
Glo - ry re - veal - ing
Org-ler og klok-ker hør-tes; kon-gen så sig om. Kon - gen hen-før -
Or-gans and chimes were peal-ing; To the king it seem'd Glo - ry re - veal -
Kon - gen hen-før - tes
Glo - ry re - veal - ing
Molto più lento
trem.
pp
ten.
dim.
una corda
tre corde.
tes, kon-ges hen-før - tes.
ing, glo - ry re - veal - ing.
pp
ff
Andante molto e religioso
BARITONE SOLO
Her er grun-nen fun-nen, fun-nen, tem-pel-hvel-vet tros-ser hel-ved.
Here foun-da-tion gives re-li-ance Tem-ple arch bids Hell de-fi - ance

mf
Ån - den bæ - ver hjer - tet fyl - des, her den stør - ste kun kan hyl - des.
Hearts are swell-ing, Spir - its glow-ing, On the high-est praise be - stow - ing.
mf
p
cresc.
Gid min tro stå fast som grun-nen, sti - ge ren som jø - kel-run - nen,
Would my faith be firm - ly found-ed Like the gla-cier pure - ly round-ed,
pp
cresc.
f
ff
ån-den nå na - tur - ens høi - de, fyldt av Ham som sam-men-føi - de.
Spir-it na-ture's height at-tain-ing Fill'd by Him all things sus-tain-ing.
f
ff
mf
f
O - lafs bøn vi al - le ta - ge nu som da og al - le da - ge. Ån - den bæ-ver
O - laf's pray'r by all ac-cept-ed Now and on in us re-flect - ed, Hearts are swell-ing,
f
f
marc.

mf
hjer - tel fyl - des, her den stør-ste kun kan hyl - des. Gid min tro stå fast som grun-nen,
Spir-its glow-ing, On the high-est praise be-stow-ing. Would my faith be firm-ly found-ed
sti - ge ren som jø - kel-run-nen. Ån-den nå nat - ur-ens høi - de
Like the gla-cier pure - ly round - ed. Spir - it na-ture's height at - tain - ing
cresc.
Lento
ff sempre
fyldt av Ham som sam-men-føi-de. Fyldt av Ham, fyldt av Ham!
Fill'd by Him all things sus-tain-ing. Fill'd by Him, Fill'd by Him!

Den norske sjømann

The Norwegian Seaman

Norwegian by Bj. Bjørnson
English by A.H. Palmer

S.A.T.B.

EDVARD GRIEG

2. Den vesle fiskerbåt
har båret frem så mangen dåd
av mot og herlig kløkt
skjønt aldri den blev trykt.
Og mangen sjømanns liv
fikk dødens krans av tang og siv,
:som burde hatt i gull
sitt navn blandt heltekull:

3. Hurra for dem idag
som farer under norske flagg!
Hurra for losen som
dem først imøte kom!
Hurra for dem som ror
sin fiskerbåt på hav og fjord!
: Hurra for alles lyst,
vår skjæromkranste kyst!:

2. But fishing-boats in need
Have shown so many a daring deed
Of courage fine and skill,
Though unrecorded still.
And many a seaman's head
A wreath of sea-weed wore when dead,
:Whose name should shine in gold
Among great heroes bold:

3. Hurrah for them today
Who the Norwegian flag display!
Hurrah for pilots true
Who forth to meet them flew!
Hurrah for them who ply
Their fishing-boats 'twixt sea and sky!
:Hurrah for all our boast,
Our skerry-skirted coast!:

Olaf Trygvason

S.A.T.B.

Norwegian by Bj. Bjørnson
English by J. E. Vanstrom

F. A. REISSIGER
Arr. by Frederick Wick

On his return to Norway from foreign exploits, Olaf Trygvason, Norway's first Christian king, about A.D. 1000, was waylaid by united enemy forces at the island Svolder in the Baltic and slain on board his flagship "Ormen Lange" (literally "The Long Serpent," "Lange" pronounced in two syllables as if it were spelled "Länga.") The larger part of his great fleet had sailed ahead and tarried at Sole (near the present city of Stavanger) in vain awaiting his arrival.

hav, mot Dan-mark: Kom - mer ik-ke O-laf Tryg-va-son?
sea towards Den-mark: What is keep-ing O-laf Tryg-va-son?
hav, mot Dan-mark: Kom-mer ik-ke O-laf Tryg-va-son?
sea towards Den-mark: What is keep-ing O-laf Tryg-va-son?
2. Seks og fem-ti de dra-ger lå, sei-le-ne falt, mot Dan-mark
2. Six and fif-ty of war-ships lay, Fold-ing their sails, toward Den-mark
2. Seks og fem-ti de dra-ger lå, sei-le-ne falt, mot Dan-mark
2. Six and fif-ty of war-ships lay, Fold-ing their sails, toward Den-mark

Hvor bli-ver Or-men
Why tar-ries Or men
så sol-bren-te menn; da steg det: „Hvor bli-ver Or-men Lan-ge, Or-men, Or-men
stare sun-scorch-ed men, Then cried they: "Why tar-ries Or-men Lan-ge, Or-men, Or-men
så sol-bren-te menn; da steg det: „Hvor bli-ver Or-men, Or-men
stare sun-scorch-ed men, Then cried they: Why tar-ries Or-men, Or-men
„Hvor bli-ver Or-men Lan-ge, Or-men, Or-men
Why tar-ries Or-men Lan-ge, Or-men, Or-men
cresc.
rit.
Lan-ge? Kom-mer ik-ke O-laf Tryg-va-son?" 3. Men da
Lan-ge? What is keep-ing O-laf Tryg-va-son? 3. But when
f
Lan-ge? Kom-mer ik-ke O-laf Tryg-va-son?" 3. Men da
Lan-ge? What is keep-ing O-laf Tryg-va-son? 3. But when

sol i det an - net gry steg av hav u - ten mast mot
sun on the sec - ond day Saw the wa - ter - y mast - less
sol i det an - net gry steg av hav u - ten mast mot
sun on the sec - ond day Saw the wa - ter - y mast - less
sky, blev det som storm å hø - re:
way, Loud as a storm it sound - ed:
som storm „Hvor bli - ver
a storm Why tar - ries
sky, blev det som storm å hø - re:
way, Loud as a storm it sound - ed:
„Hvor bli - ver Or - men
Why tar - ries Or - men

„Hvor bli - ver Or - men Lan - ge? Hvor bli - ver Or - men
Why tar-ries Or - men Lan - ge? Why tar-ries Or - men
Or - men Lan - ge?
Or - men Lan - ge?
Hvor bli - ver Or - men
Why tar - ries Or - men
„Hvor bli - ver Or - men Lan - ge? Hvor?
Why tar-ries Or - men Lan - ge? Why?
Lan - ge?
Lan - ge?
Hvor bli - ver Or - men, Or - men
Why tar - ries Or - men, Or - men
poco accel.
ff
rit.
Lan-ge? Hvor bli-ver Or-men Lan-ge? Kom-mer ik - ke O - laf Tryg - va - son?"
Lan-ge? Why tar-ries Or-men Lan-ge? What is keep-ing O - laf Tryg - va - son?
Lan-ge, Hvor?
Lan-ge, Why?
Kom - mer
What is
Hvor?
Why?
Kom-mer ik - ke O - laf Tryg - va - son?"
What is keep-ing O - laf Tryg - va - son?
Lan-ge? Hvor bli-ver Or-men Lan-ge?"
Lan-ge? Why tar-ries Or-men Lan-ge?

Piu lento
al - le stod;
all men stood;
4. Stil - le, stil - le i sam - me stund al - le stod; ti fra
4. Si - lent, si - lent in anx-ious mood all men stood; For the
al - le stod;
all men stood;
4. Stil - le, stil - le i sam - me stund al - le stod; ti fra
4. Si - lent, si - lent in anx-ious mood all men stood; For the
Piu lento
skvul - pet som sukk om flå - ten: „Ta - gen er
sobb'd out the trag - ic sto - ry: "Tak - en is
ha - vets bunn skvul - pet som sukk om flå - ten:
o - cean deep sobb'd out the trag - ic sto - ry:
skvul - pet som sukk om flå - ten: „Ta - gen er
sobb'd out the trag - ic sto - ry: "Tak - en is
ha - vets bunn skvul - pet som sukk om flå - ten: „Ta - gen er
o - cean deep sobb'd out the trag - ic sto - ry: "Tak - en is

Tempo I
Or-men Lan-ge; fal - len er O - laf Tryg - va-son!,, 5. Si - den
Or-men Lan-ge, Fall - en is O - laf Tryg - va-son!" 5. Thus for
Or-men Lan-ge; fal - len er O - laf Tryg - va-son!,, 5. Si - den
Or-men Lan-ge, Fall - en is O - laf Tryg - va-son!" 5. Thus for
Or - men Lan- ge; fal - len er
Or - men Lan- ge, Fall - en is
Tempo I
ef - ter i hun- dre år, nor - ske ski - be til føl - ge får, helst
more than a hun-dred years, Sounds in ev - er - y sea-man's ears, Chief-
ef - ter i hun- dre år, nor - ske ski - be til føl - ge får, helst
more than a hun-dred years, Sounds in ev - er - y sea-man's ears, Chief-

Piu lento
rit.
pp
ppp
dog i må - ne - net - ter: „Ta - gen er Or - men Lan - ge,
- ly on moon - lit wa - ters: "Tak - en is Or - men Lan - ge,
Helst dog i må - ne - net - ter:
Chief - ly on moon - lit wa - ters:
dog i må - ne - net - ter: „Ta - gen er Or - men Lan ge,
- ly on moon - lit wa - ters: "Tak - en is Or - men Lan - ge,
Helst dog i må - ne - net - ter: „Ta - gen er
Chief - ly on moon - lit wa - ters: "Tak - en is
fal - len er O - laf Tryg - va - son!"
Fall - en is O - laf Tryg - va - son!"
fal - len er O - laf Tryg - va - son!"
Fall - en is O - laf Tryg - va - son!"
fal - len er O - laf Tryg - va - son!"
Fall - en is O - laf Tryg - va - son!"
fal - len er O - laf Tryg - va - son!"
Fall - en is O - laf Tryg - va - son!"

Norrøna-kvad

Song to the Norsemen

From "Sigurd Jorsalfar"★

Baritone Solo and Chorus of Mixed Voices

Norwegian by Bj. Bjørnson
English by J.E. Vanstrom

EDVARD GRIEG

★"Sigurd the Crusader"

æ - ren ø - ker fol - kets ar - beid, æ - ren
styr - te tan - ke - ne og ti - den, styr - te
Ev - 'ry Norse-man shares this hon - or, Ev - 'ry
Now en-thron'd to reign for - ev - er, Now en -
ø - ker fol - kets ar - beid. Da vi
tan - ke - ne og ti - den. Kvin-nens
Norse-man shares this hon - or. As they
thron'd to reign for - ev - er. Maid-en's
kom fra Jor - sal - to - get, tend-tes san - gens al - le bau - ner og vår
krav til un - ger - sven - nen nu blev mot til man - dig i - drett, mo-rens
came, the bold Cru - sa - ders, Ev - 'ry bea - con flash'd the mes - sage, And our
chal - lenge to her lov - er Now in - spires his man - ly cour - age. Moth-er's
ung dom stod om lu - en, og det ly - ste langt av lan - det.
krav til si - ne søn - ner nu blev mål med ef - ter - mæ - le.
young men saw the sig - nal Throw-ing rays of light far yon - der.
pray'rs for sons and daugh-ters Made each Norse-man true in spir - it.
p
p
p
f
f

CHORUS IN UNISON
Nor-rø-na fol-ket det vil fa-re, det vil fø-re kraft til
From Nor-dic shores a folk is far-ing, To im-part its strength to
an-dre! Kam-pens gla-vin kas-ter gjen-glans,
oth-ers! Beam-ing sword re-flects its glam-our,
æ-ren ø-ker fol-kets ar-beid, æ-ren ø-ker fol-kets
Ev-'ry Norse-man shares this hon-or, Ev-'ry Norse-man shares this
ar-beid.
hon-or.
1st Verse
1st Verse

2nd Verse
æ - ren ø - ker fol - kets ar - - - -
Ev - 'ry Norse - man shares this hon - - - -
2nd Verse
3 3 3 3 3 3 3 3
beid.
or.

Konge-kvad

The King Song

From "Sigurd Jorsalfar"

Baritone Solo and Chorus of Mixed Voices

Norwegian by Bj. Bjørnson
English by J. E. Vanstrom

EDVARD GRIEG

Recit.
Men, er det dåd-løst at byg-ge sit land, og at væk-ke dets kraft som en vår av sin
But, is it deed-less to cher-ish your land and a-wak-en its strength like a spring from its
dva - le? Dåd-løst at væ - re den mæg-ti - ge mand, som kan mæt-te de hung-ri - ge
slum-ber? Deed-less to here be the guid-ing right hand, Who will feed all the hun-ger-ing
mf
vivace
da - le?
num-bers?
f
Dåd-løst til kam - pen på land og om strand
Deed-less to strug - gle on land and on sea
At gi tu-sin-de ar-me fra kri-ge-ne spa-ret, slæg-ter-nes slæg-ter, et vok-sen-de
And save thou-sands of liv-ing from war's des-o-la-tion, Homes for our kin-dred, A pros-per-ous
fz

dim.
land med vor kjær-lig-hed til det be - va - ret?
land, with our love and our life's con-se - cra - tion?
dim.
rit.
Andante maestoso
fz
mf
Hil jer skud av Ha-ralds-stam-men, hil jer, bol-de
Hail ye; sons of Har-ald's king-dom, Hail ye; va-liant
f
kon - ge brø - dre, en med fre - dens fa - gre vin - ding, en med kam-pens
king - ly broth - ers; One with friend-ship's crown of lau - rel, One with com - bat's
p
sei - ers-kro - ne; Nor-ges for-tid, Nor-ges frem-tid i de tven - des
crown of vic - t'ry; Nor-way's Sa - ga, Nor-way's fu - ture In your hands and

cresc.
f
hånd-tag træf-fes, Hil jer skud av Har-alds-stam-men, hil jer!
hearts u-nit-ed, Hail ye, sons of Har-ald's king-dom, hail ye!
cresc.
f
cresc.
CHORUS
SOP.
ALTO
Hil jer skud av Ha-ralds-stam-men, hil jer bol-de kon-ge-brø-dre,
Hail ye, sons of Har-ald's king-dom, Hail ye, val-iant king-ly broth ers;
TEN.
BASS
en med fre-dens fa-gre vin-ding, en med kam-pens sei-ers-kro-ne.
One with friend-ship's crown of lau-rel, One with com-bat's crown of vic-t'ry.

p
Nor - ges for - tid, Nor - ges frem-tid i — de tven-des hånd - tag træf - fes;
Nor-way's Sa - ga, Nor-way's fu - ture In — your hands and hearts u - nit - ed.
hil jer bol-de kon-ge brø - dre, hil — jer!
Hail ye, val-iant king-ly broth-ers, hail — ye!
Hil jer! Hil jer! Hil! Hil! Hil!
Hail ye! Hail ye! Hail! Hail! Hail!

Se, Norges blomsterdal!

See Norway's Flowery Vale

S.A.T.B.

2. Hør fjellets stolte foss!
Nyss brøt den vintrens bånd og tvang,
nu går den fritt sin gang
og brummer bass til oss:
Tra, la, la, o.s.v.
Ja, lystelig det er i nord, o.s.v.

3. På friske grønne eng
står blommer røde, gule, blå
og reder alfer små
en yndig brude-seng
Tra, la, la, o.s.v.
Ja, lystelig det er i nord, o.s.v.

4. Og får vi enn en skur
litt regn gjør bondens aker godt;
vi skyet aldri vådt;
det er mot vår natur.
Tra, là, la, o.s.v.
Ja, lystelig det er i nord, o.s.v.

2. Hear booming waterfall,
Just freed from winter's harsh restraint,
Its thunder now no feint,
In "basso" sounds its call:
Tra, la, la, etc.
The north much mirth and joy, etc.

3. And on the verdant field
Stand flowers, yellow, blue and red
And make the cutest bed
For little elves to shield.
Tra, la, la, etc.
The north much mirth and joy, etc.

4. And should there come some rain
That's what the farmer's field must get;
We never shunn'd the wet;
'Twould go against our grain.
Tra, la, la, etc.
The north much mirth and joy, etc.

Andr. Åbel. Carl G.O. Hansen

Når fjordene blåner

Fjords Like Violets Blue

Norwegian by John Paulsen
English by O.T. Arneson

S.A.T.B.

ALFRED PAULSEN
Arr. by F. Wick

tro-sten fra gran-li-en syn-ger der-til, da rø-res
birds in the branch-es are war-bling with glee, I mur-mur
MEL.
tro-sten den syn-ger, da rø-res mitt bryst, da
when birds are war-bling I mur-mur this pray'r, I
MEL.
rit.
SOLO
Alto or Bar.
Andante cantabile
Hm
rø-res mitt bryst, da blott hvis-ke jeg kan: Gud sig-ne dig Nor-ge, mitt
mur-mur this pray'r, As en-chant-ed I stand: God bless thee, old Nor-way, my
Hm
cresc.
dim.
dei-li-ge land, Gud sig-ne dig Nor-ge, mitt dei-li-ge
beau-ti-ful land, God bless thee, old Nor-way, my beau-ti-ful
CHORUS
cresc.
land, Gud sig-ne dig Nor-ge, mitt dei-li-ge land, Gud sig-ne dig
land, God bless thee, old Nor-way, my beau ti ful land, God bless thee, old
BASS
Gud sig-ne Nor-ge, mitt
God bless thee, Nor-way old
Tempo I
Nor-ge, mitt dei-li-ge land. Men når jeg ser fol-ket som
Nor-way, my beau-ti-ful land. But when I con-sid-er the
Nor-ge, mitt dei-li-ge land.
Nor-way, my beau-ti-ful land.

ryd - der den jord, som vir - ker på fjell og ved
peo - ple who toil, For hum - ble re - ward from the
f
fis - ke - rik fjord; de tu - sen - e menn som til sjøs og til lands, i
sea or the soil; The thou - sands who la - bor in coun - try and town, And
p
ar - bei - dets sved vin - ner Nor - ge en krans; de tu - sen - e kvin - ner som
weave for the brow of old Nor - way a crown; The wo - men who dai - ly un -
f
yn - dig og tro med kjær - lig - het sys - ler i hjem - li - vets bo, da
self - ish and true With lov - ing de - vo - tion their du - ties pur - sue, I
ff
svin - ger jeg hat - ten, da hjert - et får tolk: Hur - ra for mitt bra - ve, mitt
shout as my hat I ex - ult - ant - ly wave: Hur - rah for my peo - ple so
rit.
kraf - ti - ge folk! Hur - ra, for mitt folk, for mitt kraf - ti - ge folk!
stur - dy and brave! Hur - rah for my peo - ple so stur - dy and brave!

Jeg vil verge mitt land

I Will Safeguard My Land

S.A.T.B. G. TISCHENDORF

2. Her er sommersol nok,
her er sædejord nok,
:bare vi: hadde kjærlighet nok.
Her er diktende trang
gjennem arbeidets gang
til å løfte vårt land
til å løfte vårt land
blott vi løfter i flokk.

3. Denne bostavn er vår
og vi elsker den for
hvad den var, hvad den er
hvad den bliver igjen.
Og som kjærlighet gror
av den hjemlige jord,
skal den gro av vor kjærlighets
frøkorn igjen.

Bj. Bjornson.

2. Here is sunshine enough,
Here is subsoil enough,
Were our love but enough
For the task to be done.
Here is will to aspire
Through our work, and desire
To develop our land
If we all act as one.

3. This our homestead, and more
We are loving it for
What it was, what it is,
What the future will show.
And as love grows apace
On the cherished home place
From the seed of our love
It shall constantly grow.

John Heitmann.

Brudeferden i Hardanger

A Bridal Party at Hardanger

S. A. T. B.

H. KJERULF

2. Så drager de fremad med lystelig spill
henover den blinkende flate,
og båt efter båt sig slutter dertil
med bryllupsgjester så glade.
Det blåner fra kløft, det skinner fra bre,
det dufter fra blomstrende apaltre.
Ærverdig står kirken på tangen
og signer med klokkeklangen.

A Munch.

2. *And thus they row onward with music gay,*
Their way o'er the bright waters wending;
And boat after boat makes up the array,
The guests all in gladness contending.
The clefts all look blue, the mountain-tops shine,
Sweet fragrance comes down from the apple and pine;
The bells in the church-tower ringing,
Rich blessings from God are bringing.

R. B. Anderson.

Gud signe Norigs land

God Bless Our Native Land

S.A.T.B.

OSCAR BORG
Arr. by F. W.

2. Me fekk det høgt og frit,
me fekk det vent og vidt
med hav og fjell.
Det stend so trygt og godt,
det stend so reint og blått,
rett som eit gudeslott
med solskinstjeld.

3. Her stig det stort og blått,
vårt fagre heimlands slott
med tind og tårn.
Og som det ervdest ned,
alt fagrar' led for led,
det byggjast skal i fred
åt våre born.

Arne Garborg

2. We got it fair and free
With mountain and with sea,
So broad and high.
It stands so fast and true,
It stands so clear and blue,
Almost divine to view
'Neath sunny sky.

3 It is our dearest lot,
It is our dearest thought,
Our trust and thrift.
Great men they were and brave
Who unto us it gave
A home for us to have,
A freedom gift.

Torgeir Edland.

Norges beste vern og feste

The Mountains of Norway

S. A. T. B.

H. WERGELAND
English version by R. B. Anderson

H. KJERULF

Ved Rondane

Home-coming at Rondane

Norw. Text: A.O. Vinje
Eng. Text: R.H. Elkin

S.A.T.B.

EDVARD GRIEG
Arr. by F.W.

Gud signe vårt dyre Fedraland

Hymn to Norway

S. A. T. B.

C. E. F. WEYSE
Arr. by F. W.

2. No er det i Norig atter dag
med vårsol og song i skogen.
Um sædet enn gror på ymist lag,
det brydder då etter plogen.
Så signe då Gud det gode såd
til groren eingong er mogen.

Elias Blix.

2. *In Norway Thy light now shines again,*
In forests the birds are singing.
Though growth of the seed is not amain,
Yet sprouting is now beginning.
Then bless Thou, O God, both sower and seed,
So a harvest it may be bringing!

Haldor Hanson.

Syng kun i din ungdoms vår

Sing When in the Spring of Youth

S. A. T. B.

SILCHER

2. Håret gråner, sangens elv
flyter mere stille,
rinner, før du vet det selv,
ut i minnets kilde.
Søtt er da hvert ungdoms kvad,
som en røst, vemodig, glad,
i de tause lunde.

J. D. Behrens.

2. *When the hair is turning gray,*
Muted be the singing,
Songs then softly take their way
Into mem'ries swinging.
Sweet is then each old refrain,
Sad, still joyous ev'ry strain,
In the silent forest.

Carl G. O. Hansen.

Aftensolen

Sunset

S. A.T.B.

C.H. RINCK

Andantino

2. Ikkun bekkens vove
risler saktelig,
gjennem mark og skove
frem den slynger sig.

3. Ingen aften bringer
stansning i dens fjed,
ingen klokke ringer
den til ro og fred.

4. Så mitt hjerte stunder
i sin kjærlighet,
til jeg engang blunder
i en evig fred.

H. Hoffmann.

2. But the brooklet's billow
Murmur on and on;
There, 'mong break and willow,
Day is never done.

3. Evening never bringeth
Less'ning in its pace;
Curfew never ringeth
Ending in its race.

4. So my heart is beating
In unending love,
Until, death defeating,
I find peace above.

Siver Serumgard.

Tilfjells over bygden

I Long to Climb the Mountain High

S.A.T.B.

H.KJERULF
Arr. by F. W.

2. Der er på veien en dunkel lund
hvor alvene er til huse.
Husk, der må du gå med lukket munn,
selv nøkken derinne later kun
sakte sin harpe bruse.

3. Men oppe på fjellet er det klang
som gjenlyder i det fjerne.
Der klinger bjeller og lokkesang;
med langelek der på setervang
sitter min fagre terne.

Welhaven.

2. *We find on the way a shady grove,*
The elves are delighted to stay there;
But mind that with lips well closed you rove,
All noises there from the bright elves drove;
Necken, alone may play there.

3. *But up on the top we'll hear a ring,*
Where echoes resound 'mong the mountains;
There bells will jingle and maidens sing,
We'll hear girls laugh, and we'll see them spring,
Mirror'd in sparkling fountains.

R. B. Anderson.

★ Seter: Mountain Cabin

Arnes sang

Over the Lofty Mountains

S.A.T.B.

H. KJERULF

2. Ørnen løfter med sterke slag
over de høie fjelle,
ror i den unge, kraftfulle dag,
metter sitt mot i det ville jag,
senker sig hvor den lyster,
ser mot de fremmede kyster.

3. Ut vil jeg! Ut! Å, så langt, langt, langt
over de høie fjelle!
Her er så knugende, tærende trangt,
og mitt mot er så ungt og rankt,
la det få stigningen friste,
ikke mot murkanten briste!

Bj. Bjornson.

2. Soars the eagle, with strong wing-play,
Over the lofty mountains;
Rows through the young and vigorous day,
Sating his courage in quest of prey;
When he will swooping downward,
T'ward far off lands gazing onward.

3. Forth will I! forth! Oh, far, far away,
Over the lofty mountains!
I will be crush'd and consum'd if I stay,
Courage tow'rs up and seeks the way;
Let it its flight now be taking,
Not on this rock wall be breaking!

Auber Forestier.

Du gamle mor

My Dear Old Mother

S.A.T.B.

EDVARD GRIEG

Arr. by Frederick Wick

★ 3rd verse may be repeated humming - *pp*

Hvor herlig er mitt fødeland

My Native Land

S.A.T.B.

L.M. IBSEN
Arr. by F. W.

Maestoso

1. Hvor her - lig er mitt fø - de - land, det hav - om - krans - te gam - le
1. How love - ly is my na - tive land, That sea-girt land where moun-tains

Nor - ge, sku dis - se stol - te klip - pe - bor - ge, som e - vig
tow - er Like cas - tle walls that in their pow - er De - fy - ing

tros - ser ti - dens tann. Ur - verd - ners gam - le bau - ta -
time's de - stroy - ing hand. Those moun-tains from the form - er

ste - ne, der gjen - nem klo - dens stor - me e - ne som kjem - per
a - ges Stand firm a - gainst each storm that ra - ges Like gi - ants

enn i bryn - jer blå med søl - ver - hjelm om is - sen
clad in ar - mor blue, With hel - mets of a sil - ver

stå, som kjem - per enn i bryn - jer blå, med søl - ver hjelm om is - sen stå.
hue, Like gi - ants clad in ar - mor blue, With hel - mets of a sil - ver hue.

2. Ja herlig er mitt fødeland,
det gamle klippefaste Norge,
med sommerdal og vinterborge,
der evig trosser tidens tann!
Om kloden rokkes enn, dets fjelle
skal stormen dog ei kunne felle,
som bauta enn de skulle stå
og vise hvor vårt Norge lå,
som bauta enn de skulle stå
og vise hvor vårt Norge lå.

S.O. Wolf.

2. Yes, lovely is my native land,
Old Norway, with her summer bowers,
Her rock-bound shores, her snow-crown'd towers,
Defying time's destroying hand.
Tho' storms the earth itself would sever,
These mountains shall remain forever;
As monuments they yet shall stand
And show where lay my fatherland,
As monuments they yet shall stand
And show where lay my fatherland.

John Dahl.

To Sons of Norway

(Opening Song)

(Mel: "My Native Land")

1. To Sons of Norway we will sing
A song of cheer and exultation.
Let it be known throughout the nation
That we are here and treasures bring:
A will to useful undertaking,
To work, promote the nation's making.
To this we'll give our brain and brawn,
But choosing to be no man's pawn,
To this we'll give our brain and brawn,
But choosing to be no man's pawn.

2. The heritage our fathers gave
Us challenges to emulation.
Permit no fear, no intimidation
Deter us from a purpose brave!
Be strong, be kind, and be courageous!
Hold truth and honor advantageous!
Thus did our fathers do of yore,
The creed of Norsemen evermore,
Thus did our fathers do of yore,
The creed of Norsemen evermore.

Carl G.O. Hansen.

Vi vandrer med freidig mot

We Wander With Spirits High

Så synger vi på vår tur

1. Så synger vi på vår tur
i Norges herlige natur,
la tonen sig stille slynge,
som farve frem over gynge
på fjord, mot strand og skog og fjell
og blåne i naturens vell.

2. Se kyster av bare skjær
med måker, hval og fiskevær
og fartøi innunder øen,
men båter ut over sjøen
og garn i fjord og not i sund
og hvit av rogn den hele bunn.

3. Så synger vi på vår tur
i Norges herlige natur
vårt arbeid for øiet skinner,
vår fortid fra haugen minner,
og fremtid skal av landet gå,
så visst som Gud det stoler på.

Bj. Bjørnson.

To Norway's Nature

1. We wander and sing with glee
Of glorious Norway fair to see.
Let sweetly the tones go twining
In colors so softly shining
On mountain, forest, fjord, and shore,
'Neath heaven's azure arching o'er.

2. See sloping the skerried coasts,
With gulls and whales and fishing-posts
And vessels in shelter riding,
While boats o'er the sea are gliding,
And nets in fjord and seines in sound,
And white with spawn the ocean's ground.

3. We wander and sing with glee
Of glorious Norway fair to see.
Our present to labor binds us,
Each how of the past reminds us,
Our future shall be sure and bright,
As God we trust and do the right.

A. H. Palmer.

Rett som ørnen stiger

Mounts on High the Eagle

S.A.T.B.

SPOHR.

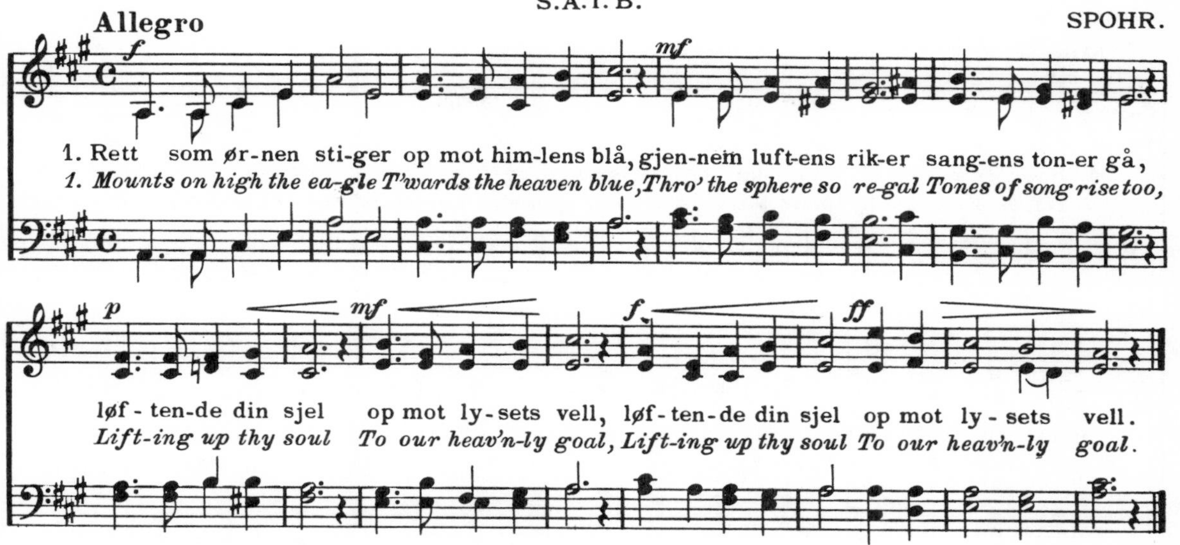

2. Alt hvad stort og herlig
for din tanke står,
Alt hvad ømt og kjærlig
helst ditt sinn attrår,
:All ditt hjertes trang
toner frem i sang.:

Johan Didrik Behrens

2. All that's great and glorious
E'er be in thy thought,
All that's good made victor'ous,
Tender love has taught,
: All for which hearts long
Rings out in thy song.:

Conrad J. Hansen.

Deilig er jorden

Beautiful Savior

S.A.T.B.

B.S.INGEMANN

Crusaders' Hymn from 12th Century.

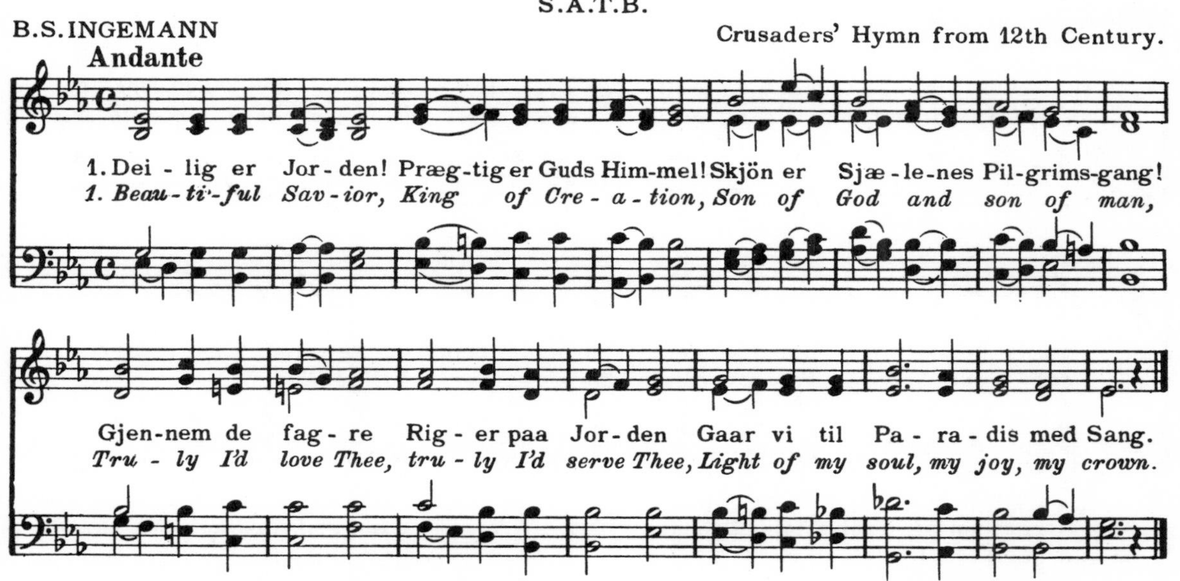

2. Tider skal komme, Tider skal henrůlle,
Slegt skal fölge Slegters Gang,
Aldrig forstůmmer Tonen fra Himlen,
I Sjælens glade Pilgrimssang!

2. Fair are the meadows, Fairer the woodlands,
Robed in flowers of blooming spring;
Jesus is fairer; Jesus is purer;
He makes our sorrowing spirit sing.

Norges utvandrede sønner

Norway's Emigrated Sons

S. A. T. B.

JULIUS B. BAUMANN | RUDOLPH MØLLER

2. Fikk Norges sol og nordlysflamme tendt
en gudegnist i stolte fedres øie,
så la dets ætlingsskare vorde kjent
som Odins gudesønner her med føie.
: La ærens fanelys i minners brand
Oss mane frem til dåd i dette land.:

2. If Norway's sun and flaming northern light
Gave to our fathers' eyes a god-like twinkle,
Then may their teeming offspring take delight
In proving to be worthy sons of Odin.
: Let banners of a glorious past, unfurled,
Urge us to action in the Western World.:

Hvor i verden jeg går

Though I Roam O'er the World

2. Og jeg elsker vel høit våre fedres bedrift,
   og hvert sagn driver blod i mitt kinn;
   dog, jeg ser kun dets kraft enn i sten og i skrift;
   den er stor, men den er ikke min.

3. O, men folket som lever med mig på en dag,
   det er mitt, er mitt fødelands lyst,
   og naturen er skjønn kun ved hjertenes slag,
   som en blomst på den elskedes bryst.

A. Munch.

2. O, I love well the deeds by forebears of my own,
   And each legend makes my eyes to shine.
   Though, perceiving its glamour in writing and stone,
   It is great, but it counts not as mine.

3. But the people that live here with me on this day,
   They're the pride of my own native land.
   And that nature is grand, only hearts can display,
   Like a flower in the loved one's hand.

Carl G. O. Hansen.

Havet er skjønt

Grand is the Sea

S.A.T.B.

Norwegian Version by S.O.Wolf
English Version by Auber Forestier

F.A.REISSIGER

Sangen

Melodi: Havet er skjønt

1. Sangen har lysning, og derfor den gyter
over ditt arbeid forklarelsens skinn!
Sangen har varme, og derfor den bryter
stivhet og frost, så det tør i ditt sinn!
Sangen har evighet; derfor den skyter
fortid og fremtid ihop for ditt syn,
ånder uendelig attrå og flyter
Bort i et lyshav av lengsler og lyn!

2. Sangen forener, idet den fortoner
mislyd og tvil på sin strålende gang;
sangen forener, idet den forsoner
kamplystne krefter i samstemmig trang,
trangen til skjønnhet, til dåd, til det rene!
— Nogen kan gå på den lyslange bro
høiere, høiere, frem til det ene
som ikke åpnes for annet enn tro.

Bj. Bjornson.

Song

Melody: Grand is the Sea

1. *Song brings us light with power of lending*
Glory to brighten the work that we find;
Song brings us warmth with the power of rending
Rigor and frost in the swift-melting mind.
Song is eternal with power of blending
Time that is gone and to come in the soul,
Fills it with yearnings that flow without ending,
Seeking that sea where the light-surges roll.

2. *Song brings us union, while gently beguiling*
Discord and doubt on its radiant way;
Song brings us union and leads, reconciling
Battle-glad passions by harmony's sway,
Unto the beautiful, valiant, and holy!
—Some can pass over its long bridge of light
Higher and higher to visions that solely
Faith can reveal to the spirit's pure sight.

A. H. Palmer.

Vingede skarer

Soft Shadows Falling

S.A.T.B. FLEMMING (Integer Vitæ)

Andante

2. Ak, om jeg kunde følge fuglens bane,
vilde jeg blunde dog blandt mørke grane,
hist i det fjerne smiler ingen stjerne
så søtt som drømmene her.

J. S. Welhaven.

2. Now let all living join and sing thanks-giving.
Sing to the stars above all your songs of sacred love.
From earth and to the sky
Strains of nature's lullaby sweetly resounding.

Fredr. Wick.

Når solen ganger til hvile

At Eve, When Sun Has Descended

SOFIE DEDEKAM

2. Da drømmer jeg mig tilbake
til fortidens gylne land,
og later min tanke drage
så langt over fjell og strand.
Jeg her til hjemmet er bunden,
men tanken, den flyver så lett;
den stanser ei før den har funden
sin kjære, utvalgte plett.

Sofie Dedekam.

2. Then dream I that I've been carried
To by-gones' fair golden land
And there my fond thoughts have tarried,
They've hovered o'er hill and strand.
The ties to home here are binding,
But thoughts will so read'ly take flight
And pause not before on finding
The lovely and sacred site.

Carl G.O. Hansen.

Ungbirken

1. En ungbirk stander ved fjorden
og vannspeilet ganske nær;
hvor stor og smukk den er vorden
de år jeg har boet her!
nu løfter den hvite stamme
kronen fra bredden lav;
men tro dog ei den vil bramme,
den vet ikke selv derav.

2. Du deilige birk, du kjære!
på dig vil jeg ofte se.
Gud give jeg måtte lære
hvad du mig så smukt kan te:
å vokse i eget øie
nedad med hver en dag,
å krone og å ophøie,
det vorder da Herrens sak!

J. Moe.

The Young Birch

1 A young birch once there was standing,
The mirror-like fjord quite near,
With growth and beauty expanding
The years of my sojourn here.
Its crown now the white trunk raises,
Up from the surface low,
It boasts not, thinks not of praises,
Its worth does itself not know.

2. Thou beautiful birch! thou dearest!
I often will gaze on thee,
And fain would I learn the duty
That thou canst so well teach me:
To grow in my own estimation
Humbler each day I live,
The crown that is worth approbation,
'Tis only the Lord can give.

Auber Forestier.

Vårmorgen

Spring Morning

S.A.T.B.

A. SCHULZ

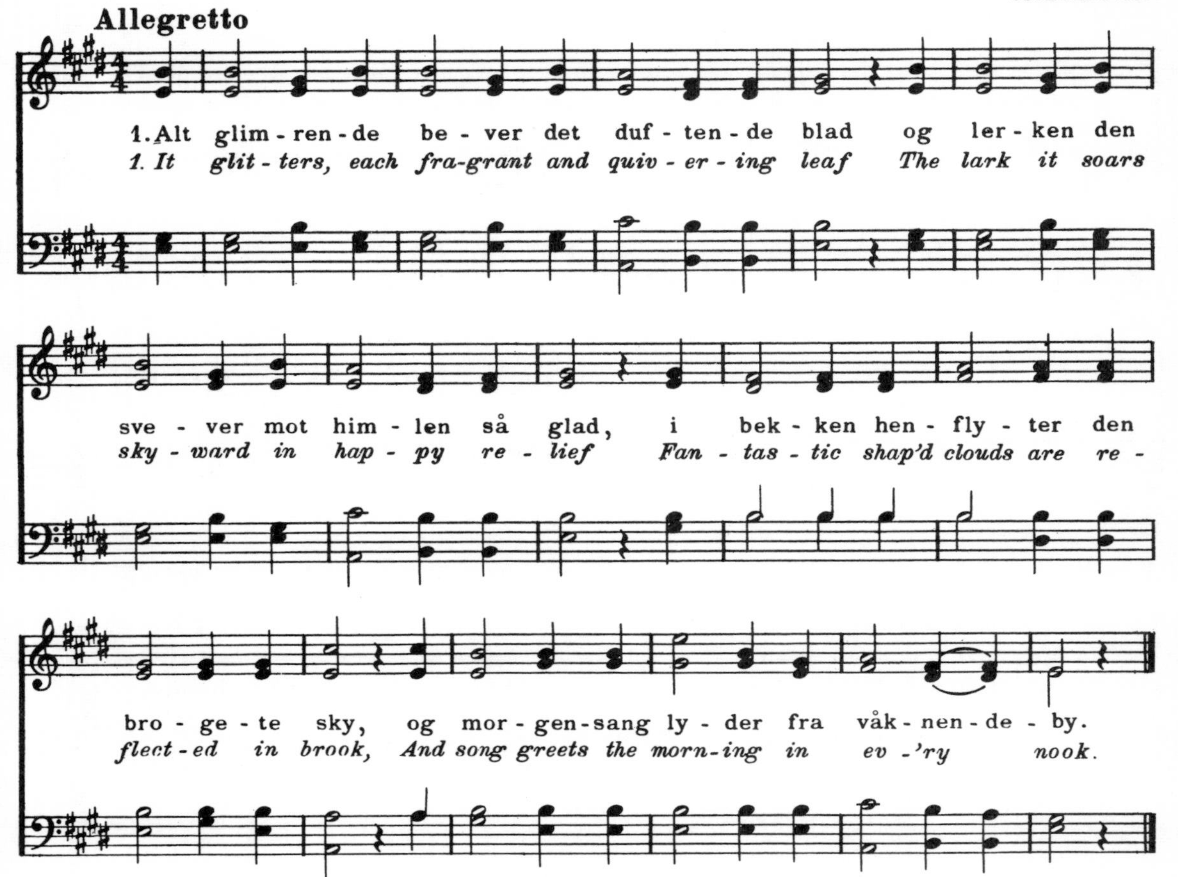

2. Og jeg vil forglemme hver kunstlete trang,
   og blande min stemme med fuglenes sang,
   snart enkelt de kveder med sorgløse slag
   og hilser med glede den kommende dag.

3. Nu solen fremstiger så prektig og klar,
   og rimfrosten viker, som gresstrået bar:
   rundt om millioner forenes i kor;
   høit hvirvlede toner: "Vår Skaper er stor!"

2. Forget will I all that seems idle and wrong.
My voice will I blend with the birds' joyful song.
So carefree they warble their sweet simple lay
And greet with rejoicing the oncoming day.

3. The sun then ascends so majestic and clear.
The coatings of frost from the blades disappear.
From millions ring out a melodious call
In praises of Him, the creator of all.

Carl G.O. Hansen.

Der ligger et land mot den evige sne

There Lies a Fair Land

2. Hun tok oss i fanget dengang vi var små,
og gav oss sin saga med billeder på.
vi leste så øiet blev stort og vått;
da smilte den gamle og nikket blott.

3. Hun strødde sin sne over fjellbratte li,
bød så sine gutter å stå den på ski.
Hun knuste med stormhånd det Nordhavs speil,
bød så sine gutter å heise seil.

4. Da lød der et "fremad!" et "fremad" ennu
på fedrenemål og med fedrenehu,
for frihet, for norskhet, for Norge hurra!
Og fjellene selv roper langt hurra.

Bj. Björnson.

2. We leaned on her bosom when children we were,
She gave us a book full of pictures of her;
We read till our eyes they grew large and moist
Then did she but nod, and with smiles rejoiced.

3. She covered the mountain sides over with snow,
And bade then her boys on their skees down them go;
She crushed the old North sea with roaring gale
And bade her brave sailor lads hoist the sail.

4. Then echoes of "forward" so loudly did roll
In ancestral speech and with ancestral soul;
For freedom, for Norsemen, for Norway, "Hurrah!"
The mountains re-echoed a loud "Hurrah!"

R.B. Anderson.

Den store hvide Flok

The Vast, Unnumber'd Throngs

SOLO and S.A.T.B.

English Version by O.T. Arneson
Danish Version by Brorson

NORWEGIAN FOLK MELODY

har sig toed I Lam - mets Blod Til
come, to meet At Je - sus' feet In
Og har sig toed I Lam - mets Blod Til
Have come, to meet At Je - sus' feet In
Him - lens Hel - lig - dom. Der hol - de de nu
the e - ter - nal home. And there ar-rayed in
Him - lens Hel - lig - dom. Der hol - de de, Der hol - de de nu
the e - ter - nal home. And there ar-rayed, And there ar-rayed in
Kir - ke-gang Med u - op - hör - lig Ju - bel-sang I höi - e Kor,
cleans'd at-tire Their an - thems sing to harp and lyre, With cher-ub-im
Kir - ke-gang Med u - op - hör - lig Ju - bel-sang I
cleans'd at-tire Their an - thems sing to harp and lyre, With
Hvor Gud han bor Blandt al - le Eng - les Sang.
And ser - aph - im In heav'ns ce - les - tial choir.
höi - e Kor, Hvor Gud Han bor Blandt al - le Eng - les Sang.
cher - ub - im And ser - aph - im In heav'ns ce - les - tial choir.

Sang til juletreet

Song to the Christmas Tree

2. Om Jesus barnet fortalte mor
så mangen aften vi satt derhjemme.
Vi kan hans bud og hans milde ord,
vi vet at aldri vi dem kan glemme.
Når stjernen skinner
om Ham vi minnes, vårt juletre.

2. *Thou bringest mem'ries of childhood days,*
When mother told us the Christmas story
How Christ, our Savior, by God's own grace,
Was sent on earth to bring peace and glory.
Now bells are ringing
And children singing His praise today.

Glade Jul

Silent Night

S.A.T.B.

2. Julefryd! Evige fryd!
Sange full av himmelsk lyd!
Det var engle som hyrderne så
den gang Jesus i krybben lå.
Evig er englenes sang,
evig er englenes sang.

2. *Silent night, Holy night,*
Shepherds quake at the sight,
Glories stream from heaven afar,
Heav'nly hosts sing Alleluia,
Christ the Savior is born,
Christ the Savior is born!

Jeg synger julekvad

Now Sing We, Now Rejoice

S.A.T.B.

J. KLUG, 1535

2. O Jesus, du barnlill,
Dig lenges jeg så til.
Kom til mig alle sinde,
tred inn om her er smått.
La mig dig se og finne.
Ak, da har jeg det godt.
Drag mig op til dig,
Drag mig op til dig.

2. *A gift from heav'n to me,*
I can not rise to Thee;
O cheer my wearied spirit,
O pure and holy Child,
Through all Thy grace and merit,
Blest Jesus, Lord most mild,
Lead me up to Thee,
Lead me up to Thee.

Astri, mi Astri

When You Were My Sweetheart

T.T.B.B.

Free translation by F.W.

NORWEGIAN FOLK SONG

Arr. by Frederick Wick

Andante sostento

Hm — Hm —

Ast - ri, mi Ast - ri som ei - ne helt tå meg den ti' eg var deg så in - der - lig god,

Out of the past, now when sha - dows are fall - ing soft - ly re - sound hap - py mem -'ries of you.

Ah — Ah

MEL.

den ti' du græt ko hver gång eg gik frå deg som du hver ei - na - ste laur - dags - kveld såg. Ja den ti' då va' eg den gjæ - va - ste gut,

Oft - en in dreams I can hear some - one call - ing, whis - per - ing soft - ly: "I love you, I do." How well I re - mem - ber those days long a - go,

in - kje eg byt - te mæ Præst el - ler Fut. Ja den ti' då va' eg den gjæ - va - ste gut, in - kje eg byt - te mæ Præst, el - ler Fut.

You were my sweet - heart and I was your beau. How well I re - mem - ber those days long a - go, You were my sweet - heart and I was your beau.

mf, p, f, rit., ten.

Island

Iceland

S.A.T.B.

FOLK SONG

2. Op til det selsomme øland drog
først våre herlige fedre.
Med sig fra Norge de høisetet tok
for å opreise det bedre.
Norrønamål de i ensomme krok
skulle hedre.

3. Skjønt våre frender bak isdekte mur
lyde må fremmede love,
kan de dog sende til Norges natur
lengselens kvad over vove.
Hjemlig det når til oss som en lur
dypt fra skove.

A. Munch.

2. First to that wonderful island, went
Norsemen, breaking the fetter;
With them from Norway was liberty sent,
There to establish it better
Saga on saving the Norse tongue was bent,
And they let her.

3. Tho' our relations on th' ice girded strand,
Live under foreign dominion;
Still they may send to their old fatherland,
Greetings on songfeathered pinion.
Glad we them welcome as kings do the hand
Of a minion.

R.B. Anderson.

Millom bakkar og berg

'Mong the Rocks

S. A. T. B.

2. Han såg ut på dei steinutte strender;
de- var ingen som der hadde bygt:
lat oss rydja og byggja oss grender
og so eiga me rudningen trygt.

3. Han såg ut på det bårute havet;
der var ruskutt å leggja ut på;
men der leikade fisk ned i kavet,
og den leiken den vilde han sjå.

4. Fram på vetteren stundom han tenkte:
gjev eg var i eit varmare land;
men når vårsol i bakkarne blenkte,
fekk han hug til si heimlege strand.

5. Og når liderna grønska som hagar,
når det laver av blomar på strå,
og når næter er ljose som dagar;
kan han ingenstad venare sjå.

Ivar Åsen.

2. To be up and to do, is his glory;
And he has to be sturdy and strong;
But 'tis pleasure to hear the old story,
Of the deeds that are treasured in song.

3. More than once does he think, in the winter:
"Would I lived in some sunnier land!"
But when spring sun on hill-top does glitter,
His heart warms toward his own native strand.

4. When each nook has its shade of green bowers,
And the nights are as bright as the days;
When the fields are all fragrant with flowers,
Then he longs for no lovelier place.

R.B.Anderson.

På1 på haugen

Paul On the Hillside

English version by F. W. S. A. T. B. FOLK SONG

Allegretto

mf

1. Pål si - ne hø - no på hau - gen ut - slep - te, hø - nunn så
1. Paul let his chick - ens run out on the hill - side, O - ver the

lett o - ver hau - gen sprang; Pål kun - ne væl på hø - nom for -
hill they went trip - ping a - long; Paul un - der - stood by the way they were

ne - me ræ ven va u - te mæ rum - pa så lang: Klukk, klukk,
act - ing; Feel - ing a warn - ing that some-thing was wrong: Cluck, cluck,

Klukk, klukk,
Cluck, cluck,

klukk, sa hø - na på hau - gom, Klukk, klukk, klukk, sa
cluck, The chick - ens were cack - ling, Cluck, cluck, cluck, The

klukk, klukk, Klukk, klukk, klukk, klukk,
cluck, cluck, Cluck, cluck, cluck, cluck,

hø - na på hau - gom; Pål han sprang og vreng - de mæ
chick - ens were cack - ling. Paul was a - ware of the task he was

au - gom: "Nå - tør' eg in - kje ko - ma heim åt a mor!"
tack - ling: "Now I'm a - fraid to go home to my ma!"

2. Pål han gjekk seg lit lenger på haugen,
fekk han sjå ræven låg på høna å gnog.
Pål han tok seg ein stein uti næven,
dugleg han då til ræven slog.
Ræven flaug, så rumpa has riste,
Pål han gret for høna han miste:
Nå tør'eg inkje koma heimåt a mor!

3. Inkje kan ho verpa å inkje kan ho gåla,
inkje kan ho krjupa å inkje kan ho gå.
E fæ gå ne åt kvenne å måla
å få att mjøle e miste igår.
"Men pyt," sa'n Pål, "e æ inkje bangen,
kjæften å mote ha hjælpt no so mangen,
eg tør'nok væl koma heim åt a mor."

2. Paul made a rush for the top of the hillside,
There was a fox with a hen in his claw;
Paul took a rock and with madness he threw it,
Striking directly the fox in the jaw.
Up jumped the fox so his tail kept a'shaking:
Paul was in tears and his heart nearly breaking:
"Now I'm afraid to go home to my ma."

3. Never again will that hen ever cackle,
Never again will she let out a peep.
Now I must go to the mill for some barley
And then of meal I will bring back a heap.
"Pshaw," said Paul, "now why should I worry:
Courage and tongue clear the way in a hurry,
I'm not afraid to go home to my ma."

Skjære, skjære havre

Cutting Grain

Kjærringa me' staven

Limping Down the Valley

2. Katta sat uppa take,
tala te sine døttra:
Kor sko me om vetten vera,
me frjøsø på vore føtta.

3. Me sko reisø te Danemark
å kjøpø sko før ei heilø mark,
trine, trine, trine, trine,
trine pepar å kødn.

2. Way up on the housetop,
Mother calls on her kittens:
What shall we do when winter comes
We have no stockings nor mittens?

3. Let us go to the south-land
Buy our shoes for a shilling;
We dont have to suffer here,
If all you kittens are willing

Hellig Olav

Saint Olaf

S. A. T. B.

FOLK-TUNE

2. Hellig Olavs åsyn skinnet som en sol,
klar satt kronen ham om pannen;
mens han kneled, lå hans rike purpurkjol
som et teppe over sanden.
Her han vilde atter i en stakket frist
bygge kirke til den sterke Herre Krist;
alt på Pinsedag skulde fra dens tak
korset lyse over stranden.

J. S. Welhaven.

2. Sainted Olaf's face did glow with heav'nly light,
On his brow his crown was beaming;
Carpet-like his purple robe, majestic, bright,
O'er the sand was grandly streaming.
And a church to build had Olaf pledg'd his word,
There to worship Christ the mighty one, the Lord,
All on Whitsuntide, from its roof should wide
O'er the strand its cross be gleaming.

Auber Forestier.

Eg gjætte Tulla i femten år

My Tulla

S.A.T.B.

FOLK SONG
Arr. by F.W.

2. Eg gjætte Tulla burt i ei li,
der var so lite te beite,
eg gjekk og lokka på Tulla mi
og etter gras monne leite.
Å hei, å hå, osv.

3. Og so kom skrubben laskandes fram,
då fekk eg kjøpmann te Tulla,
å akkederinga var 'kje lang,
å penningan var 'kje mange.
Å hei, å hå, osv.

2. I took my Tulla off in a lea,
The richest grass I was seeking;
I called my Tulla to come to me,
She did not answer my speaking.
Oh hey, oh ho, etc.

3. And then the wolf came sneaking forth,
To buy my Tulla he offered;
He asked me not what my sheep was worth,
No heaps of money he proffered
Oh hey, oh ho, etc.

R.B. Anderson.

Den norske fisker

The Norse Fisherman

2. Dog, snart går dagen og allting lett,
når dråtten ramler og lodd ei stanser,
og kniv ei hviler på maddingbrett,
og fisken op efter snoren danser;
da spares arme å bankes varme;
matkisten glemme de tomme tarme,
som skreke før.

3. God hustru hjemme ser ut igjen;
det kvelder tidlig, og kold er stuen,
i kroken setter hun rokken hen,
i asken raker, gjør ild på gruen.
Tungt op fra stranden inn stamper mannen,
tre våte trøier, en efter annen,
han slenger hen.

Claus Frimann.

Dei gamle fjell i syningom

The Mountains Old

S.A.T.B.

FOLK SONG

2. Av hav kom sjømann sigande
og lengta etter land.
Då såg han fjelli stigande
og kjendest ved si strand.
Då kom det mod i gutane,
som såg sin fødestad.
Ja, dei gode gamle nutane,
dei gjera hugen glad.

Ivar Åsen.

2. *From sea came sailor on his way,*
Was longing for his land.
He saw the mountain chains' array
And knew this was his strand.
It gave good cheer to all the boys
Who saw their native shore.
Yes, the old things have a famil'ar voice,
A voice that they adore.

Carl G.O. Hansen.

At far min kunde gjera

The Memory of Father

S.A.T:B.

D.W. RUDOLPH 1791-1856
Arr. by F. W.

2. Slik kar var aldri funnen
so langt som soga veit.
Og ordet flaug frå munnen
so godt som sverdet beit.
Du høyrd'n aldri mala
i klynk um sine kår.
Den guten kunde tala
med skjemt um sine sår.

3. Han lærde fransmann fikta
og finna riddarverd
og engelsmannen dikta
og hava sjøen kjær.
Og fremst han stod i lina
og rett han stelte den.
Frå Skottland til Messina
han skapte styresmenn.

A. O. Vinje.

2. A better man you never
Could find in tales of old,
His speech was keen and clever,
His sword was sharp and bold.
In hard times and misfortune
He never once complained,
He smiled at fickle fortune,
He laughed when sore and maimed.

3. In war he schooled the Frenchman,
And taught him chivalry,
He taught his English henchman
To sing and love the sea.
The world was his arena
His captain voice still rings,
From Scotland to Messina
He made and unmade kings.

O.M. Norlie.

Bor jeg på det høie fjell

The Mountaineer

Free translation by
Frederick Wick.

FOLK SONG
Arr. by Frederick Wick

gran - en bær, munt - re sje - les fri - sted er. Ver - dens
birch and pine, Is the free-man's hal - low'd shrine. Yes, I
tum-mel ned - en - for til min sky - høi - e bo - lig ei når.
love this home of mine, Far from dust lad-en roads in the val - ley.
f
Ah
Ah
f
Ah
Ah
Ah
Ah

Ah
Ah
Ah
Ah
rit.
Ver - dens tum - mel ned - en - for til min sky - høi - e bo - lig ei når.
Yes I love this home of mine, Far from dust lad - en roads in the val - ley.
f a tempo
Jeg med sang vil ma - ne frem hver en skatt som er skjult ut i
Here my roun - de - lay I sing And the ech - oes re - sound from the
klip - pe - nes rif - ter. Jeg er glad og rik ved den, kjøper
moun - tain walls yon - der And when birds re - turn in Spring, Na - ture's

mf
vin og kla - re - rer ut - gif - ter. Ah
work all a - round is a won - der! Ah
mf
f
mf
f
Ah
Ah
f
Sit - ter
Yes I
f
mf
f
f
rit.
på min tu - e trygg og ut - tøm - mer en gle - des - po -
love this home of mine, Liv - ing near - er the stars in the
rit.
Maestoso
molto rit.
kal, og ut - tøm - mer en gle - des - po - kal!
sky, Liv - ing near - er the stars in the sky.
Maestoso
8va
ff
molto rit.

Å kjøre vatten, å kjøre ve'

I'm Hauling Water, I'm Hauling Wood

English version by Fredr. Wick

NORWEGIAN FOLK SONG
Arr. by Frederick Wick

f rit.
er det mo - ro-samt å le - va.
I am out a-lone with Sal-ly.
a tempo
f rit.
f
slower
p
f
Helst når jeg får den jeg vil ha', då er det mo-ro-samt å
I nev-er miss one sin-gle kiss When I am out a-lone with
p slower
f
1
2
ff
largement
ad lib.
le - va. le - va, Då er det mo-ro-samt å le - va.
Sal-ly. Sal-ly. When I am out a-lone with Sal-ly.
Allegro
ff
largement
3
p
ff
rit.

En liten gutt ifra Tistedaln

Her hjemme

1. Ja, hjemme er det dog allerbest,
   ja, her hjemme!
   Man reiser øst og man reiser vest,
   men her hjemme!
   Her haver allting et eget lag,
   her haver allting sin rette smag,
   ja her hjemme!

2. Her kan jeg bo på min tue trygt,
   ja, her hjemme!
   I hus og hjem som min far har bygt,
   ja, her hjemme!
   ja, hjemme her på min odelsjord
   her fik jeg fot under eget bord,
   ja, her hjemme!

J. Olafsen

Home Forever

1. *We like to roam, but our home is best,*
   Home forever!
   It has no equal in east or west,
   Home forever!
   Here round about things are good and right
   And over all is a gracious light,
   Home forever!

2. *Upon this hillock I safely dwell,*
   Home forever!
   This home my father did build so well,
   Home forever!
   Here I alone am the rightful lord,
   'Tis mine to rule at this precious board,
   Home forever!

Auber Forestier

Uppå fjellet!

1. Hu hei! Kor er det vel friskt og lett
   uppå fjellet!
   her leikar vinden i kåte sprett
   uppå fjellet!
   Og foten dansar og auga lær,
   og hjarta kveikjande hugnad fær
   uppå fjellet!

2. Kom upp! Kom upp frå den tronge dal,
   uppå fjellet!
   Her blæs ein blåster so frisk og sval
   uppå fjellet!
   Og lidi skin utav blomar full,
   og soli drys alt sitt fagre gull,
   uppå fjellet.

Kr. Janson

On the Mountain

1. *Heigh-o! how bracing the air and light,*
   On the mountain!
   The wind here frolics in mad delight,
   On the mountain!
   The foot trips lightly, the eye it laughs,
   The heart new life and enjoyment quaffs,
   On the mountain!

2. *Come up, come up from the narrow vale,*
   On the mountain!
   Here blows a cool and refreshing gale,
   On the mountain!
   The slope is cover'd with shining flow'rs,
   The sunshine bathes them in golden show'rs,
   On the mountain!

Auber Forestier

Jeg lagde mig så silde

I Laid Me Down to Rest

2. Jeg klappede henne på hviten kinn,
som før var så rosende røde.
A Herre Gud bedre mig fattig ungersvenn,
her finner jeg min kjæreste døde.
Ingen har man elsket over henne!

2. Then quickly I sped to her lofty bower,
Where oft 'twas my wont to be faring;
A group of fair maidens surrounded my love,
They her for the grave were preparing.
I have no one ever loved so dearly.

Auber Forestier.

Markje grønas
Fields and Woods

Norwegian by E. Storm
English by Auber Forestier

FOLK SONG

Hør det kaller, hør det lokker
Hear It Calling

Norwegian by P. A. Jensen
English by Carl G. O. Hansen

FOLK SONG

p
ut. Med den vev - re laks i fos - sen, med den vil - tre gjet på
clime, Where in brooks the trout is play - ing And the hare roams far and
fjell, duk - ker vi i el - ve - dy - pet spring - er vi i bak - ke - hell.
wide; There we dive in deep - est riv - er, Ca - pers cut on steep hill - side.
Hjemreise fra setren
Homeward Again
Norwegian by E. Storm
English by Auber Forestier
FOLK SONG
1. Os ha gjort kå gje - rast skul - de, y - sta ost å kin - na
2. Far - væl, mark, som fe - nan gnå - gå, der e gjæt - te mang - ein
1. We have done our bound - en du - ty, Cheese we made and but - ter
2. Fare - well pas - tures where the cat - tle Brows'd, that I did oft - en
smør, nå står att å klyv - ja øy - kjenn, set - ja lås for sæ - ter -
gong! Far - væl, skog, som of - te ljo - ma tå min lur å stutt å
churn, Now re - mains to load our hor - ses And the dai - ry lock to
tend! Fare - well woods, where oft we wan - der'd Where our song did ech - oes
dør. Kor - kje finst dæ mei - re fø - e her for hei - e hell for
sång! Far - væl, hul - der, som der bud - de! Flyt nå du ti se - le
turn. Food for cat - tle nor for hill - folks Can be found no long - er
send! Fare - well all ye moun - tain Hul - ders, In our dai - ry haste to
krist, gla æ os, os slepp åt byg - den, mei - re gla æ ku - e vist.
in: Vin - ters ti er ilt å lig - gje u - te bå for ver å vind.
here. Glad are we that home we're go - ing, Glad - der still our flocks ap - pear.
move! It is bad in win - ter weath - er, Thro' the storms and winds to rove.

Eg ser deg ut før gluggjin

I See Your Shadow Yonder

FOLK SONG

2. Imorgo fyrr hanin gjele,
—kjær søte vennen min!
ligg far bort mæ kvenne å mele,
då kann du sleppa inn.
I kvell eg gløymde no kubbin å reisa,
eg meiner den guten æ bindande galin,
som inkje kann høyre at far han æ heime,
kjær søte vennen min!
Suril, suril, suril, surilei.

2. I'll rock my little brother
Until he falls asleep;
But me there is no other
Who him can quiet keep.
And if you are freezing, pray go in the stable,
I'll send for you there just as soon as I'm able;
For father is going out soon, pray be careful.
O dearest, sweetest friend!
Hush a-baby, hush a-baby-by.

Auber Forestier

Ågots sang

Ågot's Evening Song

H. A. BJERREGAARD
Free translation by F. W.

V. THRANE

Andante

p

So - le går bak å - sen ne, skjuggjin bli så lan - gje.
O'er the ridge the sun is glid - ing, Shad - ows dark - en and grow long.

mf

Nåt - te kjem snart at - te - ve, te - ke meg ti fan - gje.
Na - ture, all in peace a - bid - ing With the night - in - gale in song.

p

Krytrein u - ti kve - e står, eg åt sæ - ter - stu - le går.
Twin - kling stars will gath - er soon All a - round that sil - v'ry moon.

Døl'n

The Peddler

Allegretto

FOLK SONG

p

Døl'n går på ga - tun alt mæ sit us - lø smør å smør, å døl'n går på
Farm - er with his wag - on is ped - dling but - ter on the street, The farm - er with his

ga - tun alt mæ sit us - lø smør. Kor vil du ha for smø - re dit end-
wag - on is ped - dling on the street. It looks to me like mar - ga - rine, But

skjønt dæ æ so trått å kvitt? Hei hop, kon - falle - ri - la - la - la, end - skjønt du æ ein døl.
I will buy some if it's clean, Sing la, la, la, la, la, la, la, la. I'll buy some if it's clean.

Kjølstavisen

The Kjølsta Song

Ola Glomstulen

Ola Glomstulen

FOLK SONG

2. :Ola Glomstulen hadde ei halv skæppe malt:.
Å kjære mi Kari! du brygger vel alt?
For i morgon ska' Ola Glomstulen gjifte seg.

3. :Ola Glomstulen hadde so lang ei bru'fær':
Ho nådde frå Solum te Gråten hjå Blehr,
For idag ska' han Ola Glomstulen gjifte seg.

2. :Ola Glomstulen owned just a half bushel malt:
O please, my dear Kari, you must brew it all,
For tomorrow shall Ola Glomstulen married be.

3. :Ola Glomstulen's wedding was a long, gay parade:
Of neighbors and kinfolks and friends all so glad,
For today shall Ola Glomstulen married be.

Her er det land, som hugar meg best

Here Is the Land That Suits Me the Best

FOLK SONG

2. Her er vel jordi hugleg å sjå
og yndeleg på alle tider,
helst når ho heve sumars-ploggi på
og blømer til dei øvste lider.
Aldri vild' eg bytt i nokon handa skatt
denne vår sæle sumarljose natt,
då jordi ligg i skrud og søv som ei brud,
og dagen vakjer trutt um landet.

2. Pleasure 'tis here the earth to survey,
Regardless of seasons' changes;
View it adorn'd in summer's array
And blooming o'er widest ranges.
No-where is there such enchanting, soft light
As we up North have on dreamy summer night;
Fair is all outside in sleep like a bride,
And day o'er the land holds vigil.

Ivar Åsen

Carl G. O. Hansen

I rosenlund under sagas hall

To Ole Bull

★"Necken": A Water Sprite.

2. Thi elven nynner et gammelt kvad,
der bæres vidt over strande,
om asers drott som ved bredden satt
og drakk av rislende vanne.
Mens sagas ånd i denne drikk
det svunne åpenbaret,
stod fremtids syn for Odins blikk
av minnets glans forklaret.

3. Vi vandrer da til den klare strøm
i sagas fredede rike.
Vårt Nordens lyseste fremtidsdrøm
vil der av bølgene stige.
Ti Odins ætt har intet vell,
der mere liflig kveder,
enn dette håp for Nordens hell,
som bor i minnets beger.

J. S. Welhaven.

2. And all of joy's and sorrow's bowl
That's found in Norway's nation,
Was drunk by him, and it made his soul
The fount of weird inspiration.
Oh hear that sweet and plaintive strain!
It calms the raging ocean,
It brings your childhood back again,
Your parents' fond devotion.

3. All hail! thou blessedest bard of song!
Divine thy bow! and an ocean
Of joy is shed on the listening throng,
Thou kindlest flames of devotion.
When nations listen to thy lay
And tremble at thy power;
Then quivers 'mong thy mountains gray
With joy each little flower.

The English Version: "To Ole Bull" R.B. Anderson is not a translation of Welhaven's poem: "I Rosenlund."

Peter Tordenskjold*

Peter Tordenskjold

Norwegian by G. Rode
English by Conrad J. Hansen

*Popular Norwegian naval hero in Denmark-Norway's war with Sweden at the beginning of the 18th century.

2. Mens i vuggen han lå svøpt,
Peter Wessel blev han døpt;
paa fregattens skansevoll
fikk han navnet "Tordenskjold."

3. Atten barn gikk frem på rad
hos hans far i Trondheim stad,
døtre seks og sønner tolv,
men kun en blev Tordenskjold.

4. Litt ustyrlig, som det går,
var han nok i barndomsår,
lærte bok kun halvt med voll.
"Heller slåss," sa Tordenskjold.

5. Nål i hånd han hadde fått,
men det våpen var for smått.
På kanoner fikk han hold.
"De går an," sa Tordenskjold.

6. Engang på den svenske strand
gikk han med sin flokk i land.
Da brøt frem et rytterhold,
vilde fange Tordenskjold.

7. En dragon stakk hånden frem,
men han trakk den aldri hjem.
Han ham trodde i sin voll;
"Dengang ei !" sa Tordenskjold.

8. Tordenskjold i sjøen sprang,
kuglene omkring ham sang,
gjennem bølgen dyp og kold
svømmet Peter Tordenskjold.

9. Tordenskjold han var polisk,
gikk omkring og solgte fisk.
Fienden bak sin egen voll
narret blev av Tordenskjold.

*2. Swath'd in cradle where he lay,
Peter Wessel named him they;
When in frigate's crew enrolled
Earned the name of Tordenskjold.*

*3. Eighteen children gave renown
To a home in Trondheim town;
Daughters six and sons twelve told,
Though but one came Tordenskjold.*

*4. Quite unruly, it was said,
Was the boyhood life he led.
Books did him but half way hold:
"Rather fight," said Tordenskjold.*

*5. Needle in his hand was gall,
For that weapon was too small.
Then on cannons he got hold.
"These will do," said Tordenskjold.*

*6. Once upon the Swedish strand,
Landed with invading band:
Then appeared some horsemen bold
Who would capture Tordenskjold.*

*7. A dragoon put forth his hand,
But ne'er pulled it back again:
He who thought he him could hold.
"Not this time," said Tordenskjold.*

*8. Tordenskjold leaped in the sea,
Bullets sang around him free.
Through the waves so deep and cold
Swam our Peter Tordenskjold.*

*9. Tordenskjold, sly as you wish,
Went about and sold them fish.
Foemen well within their fold,
Fooled they were by Tordenskjold.*

10. Rask han vokste op på val
fra matros til admiral;
ingen glans og ære gold
fikk dog makt med Tordenskjold.

11. For sin synd av hjertens grunn
bad han i sin siste stund,
gav sin sjel så Gud i voll,
sådan døde Tordenskjold.

12. Skal til kamp på bølgens topp
flaggets kors i stavnen opp,
giv der bak den røde fold
stod en helt som Tordenskjold!

10. Up the ranks above them all,
Seaman clear to admiral.
Glory, honor, nor yet gold
Difference made to Tordenskjold.

11. For his sins, to higher powers,
Prayed he in his latest hours,
Gave his soul to God, we're told;
Thus came death to Tordenskjold.

12. When rage battles on the seas,
Flag with cross floats on the breeze,
Would that back the flag's red fold,
Stood a man like Tordenskjold.

Sinklars-visen *

The Sinclair Brave

Norwegian by E. Storm
English by W. S. Walker

* During the Kalmar War, a force of Scotch mercenaries that landed in Norway, headed by Colonel George Sinclair, was practically wiped out by farmers in Gudbrandsdal in August 1612.

FOLK SONG

Maestoso

2. De bønder fra Våge, Lesje og Lom
med skarpe økser på nakke
i Bredebygd de tilsammen kom
med skotten vilde de snakke.

3. Tett under Lide der løper en sti
som man monne Kringen kalle;
Lågen skynder sig der forbi:
I den skal fiendene falle.

4. Det første skudd herr Sinclair gjaldt,
han brølte og opgav sin ånde.
Hver skotte ropte, da obersten falt:
"Gud fri oss fra denne vånde!"

5. Fram bønder, fram, I norske menn!
Slår ned, slår ned for fote!
Da ønsket sig skotten hjem igjen,
han var ei lystig til mote.

6. Ei nogen levende sjel kom hjem
som kunde sin landsmann fortelle
hvor farlig det er å besøke dem,
der bor blandt Norriges fjelle.

2. On Romsdal coast has he landed his host,
And lifted the flag of ruin;
Full fourteen hundred, of mickle boast,
All eager for Norway's undoing.

3. And all of Lesso, and Vog, and Lon,
With axes full sharp on their shoulders,
To Bredeboyd in a swarm are gone,
To challenge the Scottish soldiers.

4. The first shot hit the brave Sinclair right,
He fell with a groan full grievous;
The Scots beheld the good colonel's plight,
Then said they: "Saint Andrew, receive us!"

5. No Scottish flower was left on the stem:
No Scotchman returned to tell
How perilous 'tis to visit them
Who in mountains of Norway dwell.

6. And still on the spot stands a statue high,
For the foemen of Norway's discerning;
And woe to him who that statue can spy,
And feel not his spirit burning.

Hvor såre lite vil der til

If Happy You Would Be

Two Part Chorus or Duet

FOLK TUNE

2. Gull har sin glans og makt sitt verd,
og rang vanærer ingen;
det er rett smukt å være lærd,
men det er ikke tingen.
Nei, skjelve ei for dårens dom,
og ta så dagen som den kom,
er mer enn gull og ære verd,
og det dig røver ingen.

J. Zetlitz.

2. Gold has its lustre, great is might,
And rank is no discredit.
'Tis fine considered erudite,
But not on this it hinges.
No, care not what the fool may say
And take what comes to you each day,
Than gold, will give you more delight.
Nothing on this infringes.

Carl G. O. Hansen.

Stev
A Ditty

2. Å mina visor dei er so snåle
som borken tråvar på isen håle,
å mina visor dei gjer ein sleng,
som litle guten på skeisor gjeng.

3. Å denne visa har ingen ende,
å denne visa kan ingen kjende,
for denne visa har gjort seg sjøl,
for ho kom rækande på ei fjøl.

Nils Johansen
Melody: "Stev" ("A Ditty")

1. Å, Nils Johansen, den væne guten,
han kysste jomfrua midt på truten,
han kysst'a ein gong, han kysst'a to;
men lel va jomfrua like go.

2. Om alle jenter sto på ei line,
å fyst di grove og so di fine;
om alle jenter sto på ei ra,
je viste væl den je villa ha.

Til lags åt alle
Melody: "Stev" ("A Ditty")

1. Til lags åt alle kan ingen gjera;
det er no gamalt og vil so vera.
Eg tykkjer stødt at det høver best
å hjelpa den som det trenger mest.

2. D'er mange nog som vil domar vera
og læ åt alt som dei andre gjera,
og lyte finna dei rundt i kring,
og sjølve gjera dei ingen ting.

3. Her spyrst no minst um, kva mange lika,
mot rett og sanning må all ting vika.
Det gjelder lite um tungt og lett,
det gjelder beinast um rangt og rett.

Ivar Åsen

Å, Ola, Ola, min eigen onge

Oh, Ole, Ole, I Loved You Dearly

English version by R. B. Anderson

FOLK SONG

2. Å, mangei tår på mitt kinn hev runne,
   eg tenkte vitet det hadde sprunge!
   Å eg hev gråte so mangei tår
   som der æ dagar i tusund år!

3. Å, kjærligheta, ho kan bedrøve,
   Gud bære den, som får henner prøve!
   Å, kjærligheta, ho æ so heit,
   Ja, ho æ værre end nokon veit!

Min barneheim

Melody: "Ole, Ole, Ole"

1. Min barneheim under grøne lidi,
   der glad eg livde den fyrste tidi,
   du vart den flekken eg mest fekk kjær,
   um ut eg vankad, du var meg nær.

2. Der barnegråten so lint vart stogga,
   og ljost eg drøymde i vesle vogga;
   der mor sitt kvæde fyrst song seg inn
   og tok med sæla mitt barnesinn.

3. Og når det skymdest mot kveld i stova,
   og trøytt av leiken eg vilde sova,
   då tok på fanget meg upp han far,
   og inn i eventyrland det bar.

A. Vassbotn

I djupe dalar

Melody: Ole, Ole, Ole"

1. I djupe dalar og grøne lider,
   å, der er fagert um sumartider,
   når soli lett yver åsen stig,
   og jonsoknotti som draumen sig.

2. Eg kan 'kje gløyma dei bjørkelundar,
   der eg hev sprunge som barn innunder,
   den litle stova i grøne vang,
   der mor hev teke meg tidt i fang.

3. Og ætter gingo, og her dei hyste,
   og kjærleik grodde av smil som lyste;
   og der hev runne so mang ei tår,
   som gull hev blanda i arven vår.

J. Bøhn

I fjor gjætt eg gjeitinn

Last Year I Was Herding

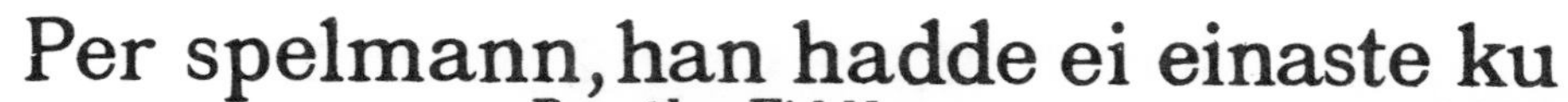

Per spelmann, han hadde ei einaste ku

Per the Fiddler FOLK SONG

2.: Per spelmann, han spelte, a fela hu låt:
:så gutarne dansa, a jenterne gråt:
"Du gamle, go'e fiolin, du fiolin, du fela mi!"

3.: Å um eg vert gammal som mose på tre:
:så aldrig eg bytte burt fela i fe:
"Du gamle, go'e fiolin, du fiolin, du fela mi!"

2.: Per fiddler then on with his fidd'ling he kept:
:The boys kept on dancing, the girls they just wept:
"My good, old, tuneful violin, my violin, my violin!"

3.: And if I get old as the moss on the tree:
:No swapping of fiddle and cattle for me:
"My good, old, tuneful violin, my violin, my violin!"

Han Mass og han Lasse

FOLK SONG

Birkebeinssang

The Birkebeiner's Song

2. Under dun å varme
hvite, bløte arme
var ei nordmanns vis.
Bruke sten til hovedpute,
når han var i marken ute,
det var nordmanns vis.

Claus Frimann.

2. Under downy cover
White, soft arms to hover,
Was not Northman's wont.
Use a stone to be his pillow
When he slept beneath the willow,
That was Northman's wont.

Carl G. O. Hansen.

Dalebu Jonson

★ Seter: A summer home in the mountains.

Akkedas millom mand å kjærring

A Domestic Argument

FOLK SONG

Manden:

2. Men med kvindfolk er så mye fjas, san,
di er bare glad ti nyt å stas, san,
kjøpety å kaffe
det må manden skaffe;
lell, så vil di gjerne vera bas, san.
Hvække svæll, san,
skjænk i kveld, san,
karfolk er di bedste folka lell, san.

Konen:

3. Ja, men karfolk, det er bare lort, san,
di vil drekke støtt å spelle kort, san,
stasen kan'te øye
på lang tid så mye,
som di på ei kveldstond speller bort, san.
Hvække svæll, san,
ro i kveld, san,
kvindfolk er di bedste folka lell, san!

Manden:

4. Ja, men hå fortjener vel dikkan, san?
Hvem må skaffe pæ-ing? Ern'te mand, san?
Øyelægge kan di,
men, min kjære Randi,
di en skjelling inte tjene kan, san.
Hvække svæll, san,
skjænk i kveld, san,
karfolk er di bedste folka lell, san.

Konen:

5. Javist karfolk nok førtjene kan, san,
men å spara, det di ern'te istand, san.
Alt det, mand han slæper,
når'nte kjærringa sjæper,
moner inte for det mindste gran, san.
Hvække svæll, san,
ro i kveld, san,
kvindfolk er di bedste folka lell, san.

Manden:

6. Men jeg sier kvindfolk er to slag, san,
no'n er leie som den vonde dag, san,
no'n vil gjerne træle,
spara, nøite, stelle,
noen er med huset likegla', san.
Hvække svæll, san,
skjænk i kveld, san,
karfolk er di bedste folka lell, san.

Konen:

7. Ja, men det er to slags karfolk au, san,
noen træler te dom ligger dau, san,
noen koper inne
å kan bare grine,
di trur hus å barn har inga nau, san.
Hvække svæll, san,
ro i kveld, san,
kvindfolk er di bedste folka lell, san.

Manden:

8. Men jeg rår dig nå te tie still, san,
du skal alti vera bli' å snild, san,
du er bra nok, Randi,
men du er bestandi,
når jeg drekker lidt, så gal å vil, san.
Hvække svæll, san,
skjænk i kveld, san,
mandfolk er di bedste folka lell, san.

Konen:

9. Jeg skal alti' stelle godt for dig, san,
når du støtt vil træle trutt for mig, san,
så skal det nok mone,
både du å båne
skal nok se, jeg gjør i huse vei, san.
Godt og væl, san,
fred i kveld, san,
karfolk træle må for kvindfolk lell, san.

Manden:

10. Vi så snildt skal stræva begge to, san,
å vi skal nok leva væl i ro, san,
mand' før føa træler,
kjærringa huse steller,
væra er jo båte vond å go', san.
Godt og væl san,
fred i kveld, san,
mand å kjærring er di bedste lell, san.

Vossevangen*

*A village in Norway.

2. For der står hassel og bjerk og el,
   og der står blåbær i lien,
   og der står geiten så høit på fjell,
   og elven løper forbi en;
   på marken vokser den grønne løk,
   i skogen flyver den ville gjøk;
   ja tro du mig, jeg sier dig:
   der er det fagert å leve.

2. Upon the hillside are berries sweet,
'Mid hazel brush, oaks and birches;
The little goats leap with nimble feet,
The river through the valley rushes.
The smell of earth and the sigh of trees,
And songs of birds float upon the breeze.
Yes, it is true, I'm telling you
'Tis beautiful in Vossevangen!

3. Der står en seljepil i dalen trang,
   der bor en hulder bak stene.
   Der faller tiden mig aldri lang,
   selv når jeg sitter alene;
   ti engen dufter og trosten slår,
   og huldren synger mens elven går;
   ja tro du mig, jeg sier dig:
   der er det fagert å leve.

3. Along the water the willows grow;
A fairy lives over yonder.
The summer days never seem too slow,
For ev'ry hour is filled with wonder.
The waters murmur, the fairy sings;
And from a thrush a bell-like greeting rings.
Yes, it is true, I'm telling you
'Tis beautiful in Vossevangen!

INDEX

INDEX — *Continued*

INDEX — *Continued*

Sons of Norway
Cultural and Business Center—
Our International Headquarters
1455 West Lake Street Minneapolis, Minn. 55408

S N
SONS OF NORWAY

THE SONS OF NORWAY EMBLEM

The dragons that came gliding out of the mists to explore Ireland, Scotland, Briton and most of Europe as well as North America during the ninth, tenth and eleventh centuries were not imaginary. These dragons were real and their bodies were the dreaded Viking langskip (long-boat) that for three centuries made their mark in most of the known world. Guided by their wits, and in good weather by the North Star and other celestial bodies, they left their land of the Midnight Sun to travel, explore and settle in all parts of the world.

Sons of Norway, a fraternal benefit society, providing membership privileges and life and hospital insurance for 21st century VIKINGS has captured some of this history and tradition in its beautiful emblem in the shape of the VIKING SHIELD; emblazoned at the top is the NORTH STAR; surrounded by the big S/N; followed by the heavens and the MIDNIGHT SUN, the rolling SEA and the VIKING SHIP (langskip) to become the finest, most versatile ship in the world at the time of these explorations, when the rest of the world was in confusion and chaos. The ship was not only capable of crossing the treacherous North Atlantic, but of skimming up shallow rivers deep inland. Evidences of their landings have been found as far inland as Alexandria, Minnesota, where they carved out a message on the now famed runestone, which says in part "Have 10 of our party by the sea (Hudson's Bay) to look after our ships 14 days — journey from this island (Cormorant Lake, Minn.) Year 1362."

The Viking Ship illustrated on the plaque is authentic in every detail. Toward the end of the tenth century, Trygvason's "Long Serpent" is said to have been 160 feet long having 34 oars on each side. Most ships however, were 80 feet long, sharply pointed on prow and stern, widening to about 16 feet amidship, with 16 oars on each side. For their size they were extremely light because all planking was clinker type, hand-hewn to leave cleats for lashing with thongs to the ribs. There was no superstructure to protect the crew from the elements except that while in port a tarpaulin could be stretched tent-like over two long poles running down the center of the ship.

The rudder or "steerboard" was on the right side where it could be pivoted up out of the way in shallow water and accounts for the right side of the ship being called the "starboard."

There was so little room aboard that all shields were stored hanging over the gunwales on each side. The Vikings were proud of their ship. The brightly painted shields, brilliantly enameled dragon heads on the prow, and for special occasions brightly colored, vertically striped velvet sails made a dazzling impression.

The Vikings were hardy and tough, fearless and fair. Their chiefs became kings and ruled with firmness and justice. The Viking Age came to an end in about the 11th century when stronger bridges were built on rivers to bar the long ship and when coastal defenses were improved and well manned.

It was then the langskip gave way to the Knarr, or trading ship, which was clumsier and slower but whose broad beam was more spacious for carrying cattle, food stuffs, farm gear and families. It was then the Viking Dragon disappeared from the seas and rivers but took her place in the hearts of men who remember her sleek beauty. All this history is symbolically represented in the Sons of Norway Shield.

So who is there among us that can say with assurance that he has no ancestor who once stood on the surging deck of a long boat, his red beard bristling as he studied the looming coast of a strange land, and who called himself ERIK. Who indeed can read of the Viking Age and not wonder if he, too, is a Son of Norway?

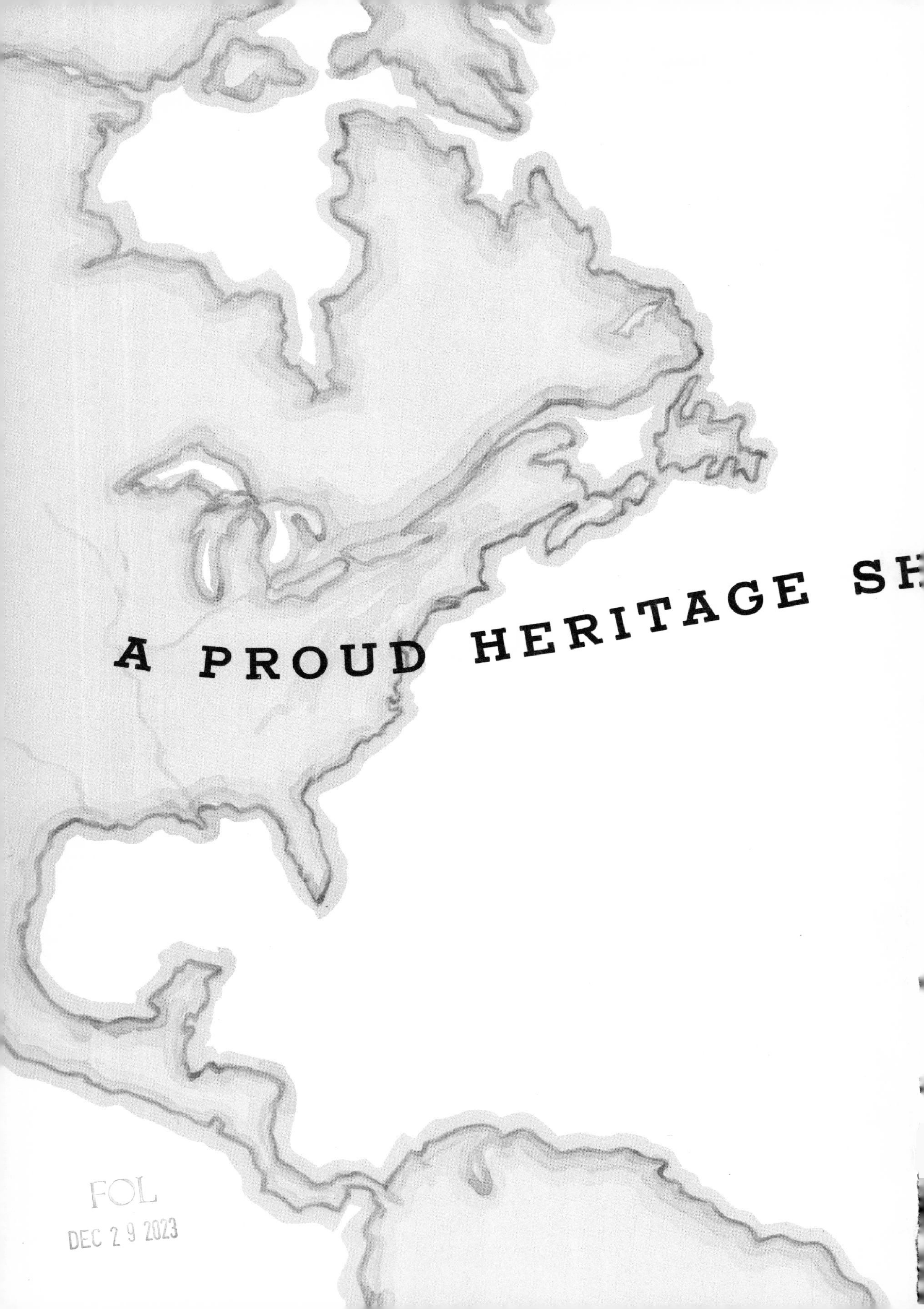
A PROUD HERITAGE SH